THE WORLD OF THE BOBCAT

A LIVING WORLD BOOK
John K. Terres, Editor

LIVING WORLD BOOKS

THE WORLD OF THE
BOBCAT

TEXT AND PHOTOGRAPHS BY

JOE VAN WORMER

J. B. LIPPINCOTT COMPANY
PHILADELPHIA AND NEW YORK
1964

Title page wood engraving by John De Pol

Contents

1252437

THE WORLD OF THE BOBCAT

Meet the Bobcat

WHAT IS A BOBCAT, or a wildcat, as it also is called? It is the smallest native member of the cat family in North America; a brownish, slightly larger (usually 15 to 25 pounds) wild cousin of our domestic cat, a silent night prowler of farm country, mountains, deserts, and even the edges of towns and cities. Its wild cousins are the much larger cougar, or mountain lion; the forest-dwelling Canada lynx; and, largest of all American cats, the jaguar, which ranges north from its Central and South American home into the southern part of Arizona, Texas, and New Mexico.

Named *Lynx rufus* by scientists, the bobcat was first described from New York State, the "type locality" for the so-called eastern bobcat, a name derived from its "impudent and abbreviated tail," as one scientist has described it. There is only one species, though scientists have described and named some eleven North American geographic races, or subspecies. The bobcat lives across the entire United States, parts of extreme southern Canada, including Nova Scotia, and south into Mexico.

Central Oregon, where I live, is one of those places where bobcats are relatively abundant. Yet only a handful of State Game Commission personnel, bobcat hunters, and trappers know much about them or, for that matter, even how plentiful they are. A couple of years ago, a local bobcat hunter put his hounds on a track on the snow-covered second green of the local golf course. He followed it as it crisscrossed the fairways and roughs, and then treed the animal

11

no more than a half-mile from the course. When told of this, golf-club members were, to say the least, surprised.

My home is situated on the southern slope of a rocky, juniper-, pine-, and sagebrush-covered butte at the edge of the town of Bend. A year or so ago, a trapper caught three bobcats on the butte, and tracks observed only recently indicate that there are others still around. Many people express amazement and skepticism when told that bobcats are plentiful in the area, that they live within sight of the city lights and, for that matter, probably do some night prowling within the town itself.

I grew up on the central west coast of Florida, learned to hunt and fish there, and spent a lot of time traveling around in the dark, moss-draped cypress swamps and the brush- and timber-covered dry hammock land. In all that time, I never saw a bobcat; nor can I recall hearing anyone talking about one. Yet, only recently, I corresponded with a veteran bobcat hunter, H. J. Nichols of Leesburg, Florida, who

An alerted bobcat watches from its rocky refuge.

A bobcat in a tree. It has been disturbed and is just about to come down.

has taken hundreds of bobcats hunting with hounds in that same area.

The anonymity of the bobcat is a basic part of its nature. It is primarily a nocturnal animal that prowls softly through the night hunting for food. Occasionally, one may move about during daylight hours, but, with the exception of dawn and dusk, they generally spend the brighter parts of the day resting in some thicket or rocky crevice.

There is a story, which I have no way of verifying, of a married couple who were walking in the woods and stopped near a pretty spot so the husband could take a picture of his wife against a scenic background. Several days later, when the film was developed, they were amazed to see a picture in which a bobcat rested comfortably on a limb over the lady's head.

I believe this could have happened, because bobcats are marvel-

13

During the day, bobcats usually "lie up" in some thicket or rocky crevice. This sort of shelter also provides relief from the hot summer sun.

ously adept at quietly blending in with their surroundings. I've often wondered how frequently people out in the wilds are under observa-ion by some hidden bobcat and never know it.

However, people have little to fear from bobcats. The last thing a bobcat wants is to get mixed up with people.

The secretive nature of bobcats has made the accumulation of information about this attractive wild animal a slow and difficult process. It is impossible to make any sort of prolonged observation of them in the wild, for they soon become aware that they are being watched, and disappear. Consequently, such information as we have about bobcats comes from many individual observations, mostly accidental or incidental, studies of the signs they leave, studies of trapped and shot animals, and the actions and characteristics of captive bobcats.

It is no wonder that many people think the bobcat is a myth, a "phantom of the forest." Many weird stories are told of bobcats, most of them untrue, and many superstitions and legends surround the animal. Immigrants to this country brought with them superstitions concerning the Old World lynx and transferred them to the bobcat. Bits of bobcat fur were considered useful as poultices for cuts and wounds; certain parts of the bobcat were eaten to cure headaches. Paws of the bobcat were supposed to help in the suppression of abdominal cramps. A bobcat's dung, used as a salve, was considered useful in the treatment of such skin eruptions as pimples, boils, and carbuncles.

It was also believed by some that the urine of a bobcat turned to a precious stone. This explained why the animal always covered the spot so no human could find it. It was also believed that a bobcat could see through wood or trees, stone or boulders. This latter belief is understandable if you've ever looked into the piercing yellowish eyes of an alerted bobcat.

One legend about the bobcat, however, is more truth than fiction. That is its fighting ability. The highest compliment that could be paid during the time of our earlier-day pioneers was to say of a man that "he could lick his weight in wildcats." It is still a valid compliment. The average bobcat weighs something less than 20 pounds. Animals of this size have been known to kill full-grown deer. Moreover, it is extremely doubtful that a 200-pound man could, bare-handed, handle one of these animals.

It takes a big and powerful dog with lots of courage to come out on top in a fight with a bobcat that may be only a third its size. I once witnessed a fight between an Airedale and a crippled bobcat. The bobcat, though badly handicapped because of his wounds, held his

15

own against the much larger animal and inflicted severe wounds about the dog's head. The fight went on for some fifteen minutes before the Airedale's owner was able to stop it by shooting the bobcat.

Several times I've seen fights between bobcats and packs of four or five hounds. The dogs, as a group, usually outweighed the bobcats about ten to one. The dogs have always won, but not without taking a great deal of punishment. I recall a couple of hounds that had holes through their paws which looked as if a nail had been driven through them. They had been pierced by long, needle-sharp canine teeth.

The beginning of a fight between a bobcat and a dog. The dog is circling the cat, trying to find an opening.

The cat is hurt but is still a formidable opponent.

The dog makes a pass and the cat rakes him with the sharp claws of a forepaw.

A bobcat carrying a mouse it will eat at its leisure.

Even though the bobcat is still little known, except by a relative few, it lives or has lived in every state in our country and in southern Canada and Mexico. The Middle Western states—Michigan, Wisconsin, Minnesota, Illinois, Indiana, and Ohio—appear to have the least; and the Northwest—which includes northern Utah, Nevada, California, Oregon, Washington, and western Idaho—has the most. In some parts of the United States it seems that the bobcat may have become extinct, although this is highly doubtful.

The bobcat is unique among wild animals in that it is equally at home on timbered mountain slopes, the arid deserts of the South-

A four-month-old kitten with strong black markings.

A three-year-old bobcat. Note the typical pattern of black bars on its front legs.

west, pine forests, and the swamps of the South. E. Raymond Hall and Keith R. Kelson, in their volume *Mammals of North America,* list eleven different subspecies of bobcats, though, in general, they are much the same in appearance, habits, and temperament. Principal differences appear to be color variations, related, it would seem, to the varying habitat in different parts of our country. Bobcats of the timbered and swampy areas show a tendency to be darker, with stronger markings, than those living in desert and wide-open country.

Bobcats have a distinctive appearance, and there is little excuse for confusing an adult with any other wild animal. Possibly, brief glimpses of young bobcats of three to four months of age might lead one to believe they were brindled house cats on the loose. However, the stubby tail should prevent any confusion. The color of bobcat pelts varies a great deal, not only between species, but at different times of the year within the same species. In general, it is a tawny brown interspersed with gray. Gray is more predominant along the back, though this seems, at times, to be more of a gray-tipped effect. Underneath, the brown color persists. The head is a darker gray-brown, generally marked with strong black lines, though this is not

19

This bobcat is unusual in that it had practically none of the usual strong black markings around the head. The teeth, like those of all cats, are highly specialized for eating flesh. (See illustration on p. 84.)

universal. The body sometimes is marked with dark spots of varying degrees of intensity, and the legs have pronounced black bars or spots. Lips, chin, and underside of the neck are white and the mouth is edged in black.

The ears are a distinctive feature of bobcats. These are light-colored on the front and inside; on the back, they are edged in black to form a pronounced open triangle with a white interior. This black edge carries out past the tip of the ear to form a more noticeable and quite characteristic black tip of hair. Another prominent feature is the ruff of fur that extends out and downward from the ears to give a rounded appearance to their heads and to make them appear much larger, especially when viewed from the front.

The short tail is, of course, a bobcat "trade-mark." The tail is black-striped on top; the tip is black on top only, with white at the

20

The ruff, or "side-whiskers," coming down from below the ears, makes the cat's head look much larger when viewed from the front.

very tip and on the underside. In warm, dry areas, such as the Southwest, buff color will often dominate and markings do not seem as pronounced. In mountainous or forested areas, such as the swamplands of the South and the timbered sections of the Northwest and the Northeast, a bobcat's fur tends to be darker, with blacks and grays more apparent. Also, during summer, the fur is apt to have more of a brownish cast than in the winter, when it seems to fade into gray.

The coats of mule deer in Oregon, living in the same habitat as bobcats, also follow a similar color change from summer to winter.

In specimens of bobcats and in photographs I have seen, the head ruffs and hair tips of the ears seem much more pronounced in northern bobcats than in those from southern areas. However, this may not be a consistent variation.

Since early colonial times there appears to have been some con-

The World of the Bobcat

fusion between the Canada lynx (*Lynx canadensis*) and the bobcat. Common names given to the various bobcat subspecies indicate that this confusion still persists; for example, the names "pallid lynx" and "desert lynx" in California, "bay lynx" in the East. In Oregon, I have found some people who insist that there are bobcats and lynx cats. Both are the same species, but it would appear that larger specimens are considered "lynx cats" and the smaller, which are undoubtedly merely young ones, are "bobcats."

Actually, the differences between the Canada lynx and the bob-

A Canada lynx. Note the lack of markings as compared with the bobcat, the somewhat longer ear tufts, and the larger feet.

The tail of a Canada lynx. The tip is all black and much shorter than the usual bobcat's tail.

The tail of a bobcat. The tip is black on top only, with white along the edge and underneath, and two or three black bars. These tail markings are positive identifying characteristics of the bobcat.

cat are so marked that there seems little justification for any confusion between the two. The Canada lynx is a much larger, silver-gray animal, with few, if any, markings. It has longer legs, larger feet, which are covered with woolly hair, and a shorter tail with a black tip. By comparison, a bobcat would appear quite reddish brown, which no doubt led to the early name of the bobcat as a "bay lynx." In addition, the Canada lynx does not have the strong black bars and spots on its legs. A positive identification can always be made from the tail, however. The tail of the Canada lynx has a black tip, while the bobcat's tail is black on top and tipped with white hairs. Although both the Canada lynx and the bobcat have tufts of hair on the tips of their ears, the appearance is quite different. With the lynx, the tufts are much longer and give more of a tassel effect. The bobcat's hairy ear tips are short and black and come to a definite point.

23

An ideal bobcat habitat: on the edge of cultivated land with plenty of brush and rimrocks for cover. This is in central Oregon.

There seem to be some differences of opinion as to how the bobcat got its name. Most naturalists believe that its short tail was the chief factor, while others contend that the bobbing motion of a running cat, somewhat similar to a rabbit's bobbing motion, is the reason. I am inclined toward the "bobbed" tail as the more obvious and logical source of "bobcat."

A bobcat's home-range requirements are few and simple. It

24

Meet the Bobcat

needs a timbered or brush area for protective cover, preferably with rocky "breaks" or canyons, and a food supply. Bobcats prefer half-open country, with lots of openings and brushy patches, to solid forest, because small food animals, mostly rabbits, are more plentiful in broken terrain.

The range or distribution of the bobcat has actually been extended in parts of the United States as logging operations have converted solid forest lands into cut-over areas. In Minnesota, bobcat range has been extended 100 to 200 miles northward as lumbering opened the country. In my part of central Oregon, I have seen the same thing happen on the eastern slope of the Cascades as timber cutting moved slowly up the sides of the mountains. When the great pine and fir forests were cut and thinned, the forest floor, bare except for a thick carpet of long dead needles, grew green with brush and young trees. Rabbits and squirrels moved into this new food supply and mule deer

Cut-over pine timber. Note the heavy growth of brush that has made good deer, rabbit, and bobcat country.

populations in the area increased as the browse increased. Cougars followed the deer, and bobcats followed the rabbits and squirrels.

With only a little of the kind of plant cover needed for protection, a bobcat can get along very nicely around agricultural areas. A bobcat conducts his solitary night hunts for the various rodents attracted to the grains and plants raised by the farmer. Although a bobcat may occasionally take a chicken or a young pig, it is generally believed that its value in rodent control far exceeds its costs in minor livestock predation.

No American animal, it seems, inhabits a wider variety of country than the bobcat. They do not often live higher than 6,000 feet above sea level, although they have been seen at 11,000-foot elevations near Mount Whitney, and in Death Valley, 178 feet below sea level. Extreme cold seems to be about the only climate they can not tolerate.

In the West, bobcats prefer to live in rocky canyons containing some trees and shrubs. These can be piñon, juniper, mountain mahogany, sagebrush, manzanita, or something similar. Wood rats, cottontails, and chipmunks, along with various species of mice, usually live in the same area. More than one western bobcat hunter has been frustrated when, after a long and tiresome chase with the hounds, his quarry disappeared into some inaccessible rocky recess in a canyon wall.

In the South, bobcats live in swamps, flatwoods, and live oak hammocks. Canebrake is also a favorite habitat. The arid sections of the southwestern desert country is to their liking where there is suitable protective cover. From an incident reported by Victor H. Cahalane, an American mammalogist, it would appear that substantial rock dens are needed for survival by bobcats in the extreme heat of the southwestern desert country. Two young bobcats from the Southwest were moved to cages at the Cranbrook Institute of Science, Bloomfield Hills, Michigan, and "without the rock dens, well insulated by solid cliff walls, they felt the heat of summer severely and died during a period of extraordinary hot weather," Cahalane reported.

26

Spring

MOST BOBCAT LITTERS are born in the spring, generally somewhat earlier in the South than the colder areas of the North. However, litters have been recorded in every month of the year.

A. Starker Leopold, writing on the wildlife of Mexico, states that the young of Mexican bobcats come along much later, and described young bobcats captured in August that were judged to be one month old and some others taken in September that appeared to be only one week old. I have been unable to find any explanation of why most bobcat litters from the southern part of the United States are born in the spring, while Mexican bobcats, only a little farther south, don't come along until late summer or early fall.

The size of the litter varies from 1 to 6 in various parts of the country. In a five-year study of Utah bobcats, Gashwiler, Robinetté, and Morris report that the largest litter examined contained 6 young, but that the average was 3.5. Embryo litters examined during this same period revealed one of 8 and several of 6 and 7, with an average of slightly more than 3. R. E. Trippensee states that the average litter in the New England states is 3 and the same thing seems to be true of California bobcats.

In Oregon, I have seen litters of as many as 5, but this seems unusual. Those of 3 and 4 are more common.

The young are born in a variety of dens, and all have in common the characteristic of providing protection and shelter for the litter. It is probable that an abundant food supply also influences the selection.

Lava outcroppings make good den sites.

In the Utah study, four dens were examined. Three of the dens were in holes or crevices in rocks extending inward some four feet, with small entrances. The fourth den was in a hollow log. Small, rocky caves and recesses seem to be favorite den sites, but logs, windfalls, root depressions of overturned trees, and similar places are used.

Sometimes the den sites seem quite unusual, though not necessarily unsuitable. A friend of mine, Fred Painter, chief of police of Sisters, Oregon, has done considerable hunting for bobcats in central Oregon and has also raised two litters of young ones taken from dens. Both dens were in the attics of old abandoned ranch houses, far out in the central Oregon desert country. Another litter he knew about had been found in a rocky depression under the roots of a gnarled old juniper tree.

Another friend, Jim Ricci, still has two bobcats, now more than four years old, that came from a litter of four found in a deserted old mining shack far out in the central Oregon desert.

Fred Painter expressed the theory that bobcats pick these old abandoned houses for two reasons. First, they don't like to dig, and an old house provides protection and shelter without digging; second,

An abandoned ranch house in the central Oregon desert. This is typical of those used by bobcats as dens.

A young bobcat playing in rocks. It is about two months old.

such places have a built-in food supply, for they are generally infested with rats and mice.

The oddest den site I have seen was located in the rocky ballast of a railroad bed. The railroad runs south from Bend with at least two trains a day. It was impossible to get into the den without tearing up the railroad, a procedure not apt to be approved by the railroad. However, I was fortunate enough to see kittens peeking out of their secure but undoubtedly noisy home, within a mile of the city limits.

Bobcat kittens, carried within the body of the female for about sixty days, are born with their eyes closed. Most naturalists agree on nine days as a normal period before they open. The weight of newborn kittens seems to vary a great deal. Gashwiler *et al.* give recorded weights of kittens from three to thirteen days old, varying from 4.5 ounces to 11.6 ounces. Stanley Young indicates that newborn kittens weigh 10 to 12 ounces. Others have given their weight at 12 ounces.

It is around twenty-one days before a bobcat kitten can use his feet well, and when about seventeen days old they show signs of play and signs of being able to see enough to distinguish motion. Kittens are weaned in about sixty days and also begin to lose their juvenile

30

Jim Yoakum with Rufus.

hair at about the same time. Substantially all of the juvenile hair will be gone within two and a half months.

The youngest bobcat kittens I have had a chance to observe were, I believe, from a month to a month and a half old. Although they were still covered with juvenile hair at that time, the characteristic black bars and spots on their legs and faces were much in evidence, as was the rim of black around the back of the ears and the tips of black hairs on the ears. Even the black tail tip with its white edging was noticeable.

All of these kittens were captured while quite young and had to be bottle-fed. They displayed many of the play characteristics of domestic kittens. Rough-and-tumble mock fights were favorite games, but rubber balls, string, and similar things came in for plenty of attention. They were quite alert to movements around them.

In each of the instances involving captured bobcat kittens with

31

The World of the Bobcat

which I am familiar, there have been domesticated animals around. The relationships that developed were quite interesting. Jim Yoakum of Reno, Nevada, raised a single male kitten in the company of a mature male Labrador retriever. The dog, a fine, mild-mannered animal, accepted the young cat without question. The kitten, which Yoakum logically named "Rufus," took on the dog as a foster parent. Rufus matured under these circumstances, and, as far as I know, he and the dog were always good friends.

On one occasion, I accompanied Jim when he took the two for a run in the open sagebrush country outside of town. It was in the middle of Rufus's first winter and there was some six inches of fresh snow on the ground. Dog and cat romped together for almost an hour. The play seemed to be mostly on the part of Rufus. The young bobcat would stalk the dog and then launch a mock attack. The dog tolerated the bobcat's play with great dignity.

Rufus obviously had a great attachment for the dog. Quite often

Jim Yoakum's Labrador with Rufus.

when Yoakum wished to terminate one of these exercise periods, Rufus wouldn't be ready and Jim would have difficulty getting him back into the car. However, a sure method was to call the Labrador. When the bobcat saw the dog get into the car, he would leap in after him.

This bobcat displayed a rather amazing reaction to various foods. Jim fed him many different things — milk, eggs, meat, etc. When the cat was feeding on milk or eggs, it was perfectly safe to pet him, but if he had eaten meat, he would revert to a wild animal and not even Yoakum dared approach him. Yoakum's method of feeding meat to Rufus was something to see. He would take a slab of meat and, with Rufus racing after him, would quickly throw it into the bathtub. The cat would make a dash into the bathroom and Jim would slam the door. He would then wait until he was absolutely sure that the bobcat was through feeding. One time he went in before the cat had finished, and was attacked.

Rufus and Lab playing in the snow.

The World of the Bobcat

One afternoon I went with Jim, the dog, and the bobcat into a rocky section west of town where the sage and the bitterbrush were thick. The two animals were having a fine time playing around, and the bobcat especially seemed to enjoy scrambling about on a small rimrock. The Labrador dug out a field mouse and the bobcat proceeded to take it away from him. For twenty minutes or so the bobcat played with the dead mouse. He threw it up in the air and tried to catch it, batted it around with his front paws, and leaped on it. Finally, we decided it was time to go back to town, but the bobcat would have none of it. When Jim tried to take the mouse away, the cat started to attack and Yoakum wisely retreated. Eventually, the bobcat, on one of his playful tosses of the mouse, lost track of it, and we were able to retrieve the mouse. Immediately, Rufus became tame and gentle again and followed the Labrador into the car without any more trouble.

A nine-month-old bobcat playing with a dead field mouse, which it has tossed into the air.

Spring

Jim Ricci, whose bobcats are now four years old, has had some most interesting experiences with them. At the time Ricci got the cats, he estimated them to be two weeks old. His dog, a male that was a cross between a Labrador and something else, accepted the young bobcats and they apparently adopted him as a sort of foster parent. At night when the dog would go to sleep, the cats would curl up with him. The young bobcats also seemed to pick up some dog character- istics, and Ricci relates that when someone would come to the house, the dog would go to the window and bark. Before long, the cats were following suit and, though they couldn't bark, would make noises.

However, they never would accept domestic cats, and to this day the sight of one drives them into a frenzy. Fred Painter, on the other hand, successfully raised a bobcat with both a dog and a domestic cat, and all three got along famously. One reason for this might be the fact that his bobcat was a female and the domestic cat was a bobtailed male Manx. Fred hoped that the two might mate, but nothing ever came of it. It is interesting to note that Stanley Young mentions two matings between bobcats and domestic cats, and the Gashwiler report men- tions one; but in all three instances, it was a male bobcat mating with a female domestic cat.

Bobcats are much more on the alert than domestic cats and appear to have a great deal more curiosity. They seem never to miss a thing and are forever investigating anything that interests them.

Female bobcats are apparently fine mothers and take good care of their newborn young, although their fear of man and dogs seems, at times, to result in their abandoning the young as they flee from this danger. It is conceivable, though probably not provable, that they are attempting to draw the danger away from the kittens. In some of the Oregon examples I've heard about, the female cat, concealed and undetected, unnecessarily exposed herself to danger. This frequently leads to the female's being killed, and when later examination of her

35

Fred Painter's bobcat playing with a male Manx domestic cat. Note the size of the bobcat's feet as compared with those of the domestic cat.

breasts indicates that she had been feeding kittens, the young are captured.

In one incident of this type, the farmer who caught the young cats that eventually were given to Jim Ricci was mowing a vast natural hayfield on a central Oregon ranch. He was resting in the shade of an abandoned old mine shack when he heard a growl, and a few moments later a female bobcat appeared. The rancher, who was armed, claimed that the cat started to attack, so he shot and killed her. It wasn't until he examined the carcass that evening that he learned of the kittens. Four of them were found the next day under a pile of debris in the shack.

37

The World of the Bobcat

Stanley Young writes: "Near the end of the nursing period . . . the male is tolerated, and, as has been stated, assists in obtaining food for the young." However, the Utah study states that "no evidence was secured that the male helps with the care of the young." It would seem, lacking evidence and observation to the contrary, that the male bobcat has a minor, if any, family life. In all of the reports I have read or heard about involving bobcat kittens, only the female is ever mentioned. Arthur F. Halloran reports that a male and female traveling together were caught in adjacent traps. This was in late February and no doubt during the breeding season.

Kittens are weaned when they are about two months old, but undoubtedly the mother bobcat starts bringing meat to the den some time prior to weaning. Between weaning and the time the female and the kittens start hunting together in the fall, there is a period of a month or two of family activity about which little seems to be known.

Generally, kittens taken from dens are still in the unweaned stage. After the kittens are weaned and are on a meat diet, the female and her litter move from the den site and begin a limited nomadic existence. At this time the kittens would normally be strong enough for limited travel. She might then move about, placing her kittens in temporary shelters in rocks and brush while she hunts. Undoubtedly it is at this time that the kittens' hunting education begins. I imagine this is a gradual process in which a cat's natural hunting instincts play an important part.

Summer

SUMMER IS PROBABLY the easiest time of the year for bobcats. The spring litters have been weaned and can travel with the female. She can move about without being exposed to the danger that comes from being too long in one place. The underbrush has taken on new growth and its foliage provides just that much more cover for bobcats. The young of other animals, especially the small rodents that are the wildcat's basic food, are in great numbers; therefore, finding food is no problem for bobcats.

This abundance of natural food in the summer makes it unnecessary for bobcats to seek their meals from a farmer's or rancher's livestock and thus expose themselves to the rancher's wrath and the dangers that result. In my part of central Oregon, one seldom hears much, if anything, about bobcats during the summer.

This is the period, also, when the kittens probably get the most important training of their lives. Though weaned and able to travel, they are not, at this time, able to defend themselves against many enemies. Nor do they have much success at hunting unless their quarry is easy to capture.

Just how a female teaches the young to hunt is something I don't understand, nor can I find any record of pertinent observations. Probably the mother bobcat merely takes the young along on her hunting trips and they learn by watching and imitating. It wouldn't take much training, for the hunting instinct is strong in all cats. The

39

The World of the Bobcat

stalk-and-leap technique can be observed as a basic part of a young bobcat's play.

Edmund C. Jaeger, in his book *Desert Wildlife,* describes the development of a family of bobcat kittens he observed over a period of several weeks. After the kittens had their eyes open, the mother would bring them out of their rock-covered den each evening at dusk. Here they would play with each other or nurse from the mother's breasts. Once she brought in a freshly killed squirrel. The kittens sniffed and pulled at it, but were too young to eat it. I believe that this is actually how a young cat's training for hunting starts.

Some years ago, I wanted to get some idea of how strong the hunting instinct is in a young bobcat. A friend of mine had three

A young bobcat practicing its hunting technique. Note how its colorations blend with rocky background.

bobcat kittens that were still on a milk diet. Just how old they were I cannot be certain, but I would estimate their age at one to one and a half months. I obtained a young white rabbit, domestic variety, and introduced it to the three kittens. All three of the young bobcats smelled the rabbit, then the lone male kitten, the most aggressive of the three, fastened his little jaws around the rabbit's neck just behind the ears. He was earnestly trying to kill the rabbit and we had to pry him loose. His tiny teeth had penetrated the rabbit's thin skin and had drawn a drop of blood. This was the first time any of these cats had seen a live animal of this kind. The amazing thing about it is that the bobcat was not playing. He obviously intended to kill the rabbit and eat it.

A young bobcat with a field mouse.

A wild bobcat in the water.

The World of the Bobcat

Ernest Thompson Seton reported that a female bobcat will carry her young ones into a tree to protect them from enemies. A friend of mine, Sam Shaver, a predatory animal trapper for the U. S. Fish and Wildlife Service, told of a time when he came upon a den located in a pile of lava rocks in the central Oregon desert. A juniper tree grew out of the rock pile only a few feet from the den, and the kittens, when he saw them, were up the tree peeking down at him. They were, he estimated, more than four weeks old. He had not seen them go up the tree, therefore he didn't know if they had climbed it themselves for fun or because they saw him, or if the mother bobcat had carried them there. Although bobcats don't often climb trees except as a matter of defense, I have seen young captive cats go up a tree just in play. In all probability, since this happened during daylight hours and one might expect the mother bobcat to be at home at that time, the family was surprised by Shaver's approach. She may have run and the youngsters, instead of retreating into the den, climbed the tree.

In summer, in the arid sections of the Southwest, bobcats must face the lack of water and the extreme heat. It has been previously noted that for protection from the desert heat, bobcats rely upon rock dens and the insulation of solid cliff walls.

Lorus and Margery Milne, in their book *The World of Night*, state that the kangaroo rats of desert country are capable of saving the hydrogen and oxygen from carbohydrates and fats and of combining them into water required for life in dry places. "This magic is depended upon by coyotes and kit fox, bobcat and badger . . . for these predators, the kangaroo rat is both meat and drink in a parched world."

While the bobcat has no great love of water, other than to drink, it is not so reluctant to get its feet wet as is its domestic counterpart. The bobcat is a good, strong swimmer and in the South often takes to the water when hard pressed by a pack of hounds. Haynes C. Alberson reported in the magazine *Florida Wildlife* that a big bobcat started

44

swimming across a lake when the hounds got too close. One dog swam after the cat, and in the fight in the water, the dog was killed. Then the rest of the pack took to the water and disposed of the cat.

I have been fortunate enough to be on hand when some captive wildcats have been exposed to water; and, while their actions may not be the same as those raised in the wild, they certainly indicate a greater willingness to get wet than one can find in the usual domestic cat. One day, Jim Yoakum and I took his bobcat and his Labrador retriever into a park area west of Bend for exercise. A small stream, Tumalo Creek, runs through the park. The water flows quickly from glaciers in the Cascades only a few miles farther east, and it is so cold that I can barely keep my hands in it more than a few seconds.

The dog and the bobcat were romping alongside the stream and the cat was soon wading in three or four inches of water as he investigated the cutbank overhang along the edge. Within a few minutes the Labrador was out in two feet of water cavorting about, and moments later the bobcat joined him. The bobcat would leap out of the water

Jim Yoakum's dog and pet bobcat playing in an ice-cold stream.

The World of the Bobcat

onto the dog and then fall back in with a glorious splash. They had a wonderful time and must have spent at least fifteen minutes in this frigid water. The bobcat finally came out simply because the dog did.

I watched Jim Ricci's cats take a swim with his two young daughters in a pond on his central Oregon ranch. He told me that the cats learned to swim as a result of their association with his dog. During one warm summer, when the cats were a year old and Jim still permitted them to run free on the ranch, the dog decided to take a swim in the pond and cool off. The cats lined up on the bank and watched for a while and then jumped in too. They liked it so well that Jim now gives them frequent opportunities to enjoy the water when the

Ricci's pets waiting for their chance to go in swimming. Note the markings on the back of the ears and the difference in the black lines on the backs of these two cats—both out of the same litter.

Summer

weather is warm. They don't like to stay in too long at a time, but seem to enjoy it. Afterward, they sprawl out on shore in the sun to dry.

A bobcat makes about the same noises a domestic cat does, only they are louder and have more authority. The bobcat snarls, spits, and hisses when threatened by danger, and these sounds, heard at close range, are ominous. It also purrs when pleased with things, and some observers say it mews. I have heard pet bobcats purr contentedly when things were going right for them, but have never heard one mew. I have read statements to the effect that the bobcat gives off a "hunting cry" when searching for food, but have been unable to verify it. Since this seems so contrary to the bobcat's stealthy hunting habits, I doubt it. I have never heard anything I would consider a hunting cry.

Susie Ricci and Tiger in swimming.

This is the size of the pupils in a bob-cat's eyes on a normal sunlit day. The cat was not facing the sun.

This picture was made in total dark-ness by use of strobe light bounced from ceiling. Bobcat had been in com-plete darkness for several minutes and pupils fill the eye almost completely. The only light part of eyeball that shows is a thin rim around the edge.

Summer

Unlike the coyote or the wolf, the bobcat seems to rely mostly on its eyes and ears rather than its nose. This is not to say that it does not have a good sense of smell, but it does not have as keen a one as the coyote.

The bobcat's excellent vision at night is due to certain eye characteristics common to most nocturnal animals. The pupil of a cat's eye is slit-shaped, rather than round, and has a much greater range of aperture. In extremely bright light, the pupil will be just a thin, vertical slit. In near-total darkness, the pupil is big and round and seems to cover the entire eye.

The retina, innermost layer of the eyeball, contains receptor cells called the "rods and cones." Rods respond to light of much lower intensity than cones and are, therefore, particularly efficient in dim light. In nocturnal animals, such as bobcats, rods are abundant in the eyes.

A third characteristic of the bobcat's eye causes "eye-shine," which most of us have seen, in domestic cats' eyes at night. A reflecting layer, the *tapetum lucidum,* is well developed and causes light penetrating the retina to be reflected out through the pupil. Reflections of light from this tapetum increase the absolute and relative differential between the object looked at and its background, thus increasing the animal's ability to see at night.

Their hearing is also superb and, oddly enough, the black hair tips on a bobcat's ears have been shown to be an aid to the animal's hearing. Apparently, these hairs act as sort of antennae and catch sound impulses. Experiments were carried on with a number of captive bobcats, and those with the hair clipped from the point of their ears did not respond as readily to sound effects as those with unclipped ear tips.

Like all animals, tame or wild, bobcats have their share of parasites and diseases. Although some studies have been made, the diseases of bobcats have received much less attention than those of game

49

animals. Bobcats suffer from intestinal worms (helminth parasites), tapeworms, and fleas. Tularemia, to which wild rabbits are so susceptible, has not been reported as a bobcat disease, even though rabbits and hares are staples of a bobcat's diet. Bobcats have been known to have Notoedres mange. This disease weakens and greatly emaciates the bobcat. Infected suckling kittens seldom survive the disease.

Rabies is relatively common among bobcats. Unprovoked attacks on humans by bobcats, of which there are a number on record, are almost always a result of this disease.

Albinism (all-white coloration), as well as melanism (all-black coloration), occurs among bobcats, but both seem to be extremely rare. The first records of melanistic bobcats were reported by Frederick A. Ulmer, Jr., who described two black bobcats live-trapped in Martin County, Florida. One was taken in 1939 and the other, from the same area, in 1940. Actually, the fur on these animals is dark mahogany-colored rather than black, and darker on the back and lighter on the sides, with the underparts the lightest. Facial stripes can be seen, and under certain light conditions the spot pattern typical of the Florida bobcat (*Lynx rufus floridanus*) can be seen. Numerous white hairs are scattered through the dark fur along the backs of both animals. The facial ruffs of these two melanistic bobcats are short and inconspicuous. This characteristic, along with their sleek, dark mahogany fur, gives the cats the appearance of being overgrown house cats. Their tails also seem to be somewhat longer than usual.

According to Ulmer, "Warmth and moisture are factors in producing melanism."

Albinism in bobcats, as in most wild animals, is probably rare. Since albinos are so conspicuous, their ability to hide and to hunt unobserved is drastically hampered. This undoubtedly reduces their chances for survival. Stanley Young reports seeing a captive Texas albino bobcat, but this is the only record of an albino I have been able to discover.

50

The hairy tip of a bobcat's ear. This acts as an aid to hearing.

Jim Ricci told me that among the four bobcat kittens he obtained in 1958, one had four white feet, with the white coloration extending up the legs past the dewclaws. This is the only example of partial albinism of which I am aware.

A surprisingly large number of people, at least in my home area of central Oregon, seem to be interested in bobcats as pets. I know of at least a dozen bobcats raised in captivity with varying results. Also, I received a letter recently from an out-of-state pet shop that wanted to know where it could obtain bobcat kittens to sell as pets.

In general, bobcats do not make good pets. They stand confine-

51

The World of the Bobcat

ment reasonably well, and apparently it is possible to live with them under a sort of mutual-respect agreement. But if one is looking for the kind of pet that responds to affection and likes to be petted, a bobcat is not apt to be the answer. Bobcat kittens must be captured quite young if one expects to have any kind of success with them. After they are a month old, they are hard to manage. It is best to get them as young as possible, even before their eyes are open.

Trapper Sam Shaver once told me of two bobcats that his mother took from a den when they were about two months old. She took them home with the idea of making pets of them. However, she was never able to do a thing with them, and they got wilder as they grew older.

The people who have raised bobcats successfully were either amateur or professional naturalists who had patience and understanding and did not expect a bobcat to act like one of its domestic cousins.

Jim Ricci's cats, which were about a week and a half old when he got them, make a case very much in point. Ricci, a former professional wild-animal trainer who has performed with lions and tigers, let the young cats run more or less free on his ranch as soon as they were large enough to take care of themselves. On the ranch, Ricci had

A litter of bobcat kittens.

chickens and domestic geese, as well as an odd assortment of ducks. Before long, he told me, the young bobcats had killed and eaten all the ducks and chickens, and, a little later, finished off the geese. The geese were quite large and would beat the kittens off with their powerful wings. However, the four young bobcats soon learned to gang up on them and then the big birds didn't last long.

None of the pet bobcats I have met seem to relish or seek petting or handling. They tolerated it from members of the family, but it didn't seem to be something they needed. Strangers were also accepted on a seemingly "you leave me alone and I'll leave you alone" basis. I have never felt free to pet or handle one of these animals unless someone was around with whom the animal was familiar.

However, bobcats do like to play. Ricci's two young daughters found their cats tireless companions as long as they were indulging in cat-type play. This consisted mostly of chasing balls on string and of similar activities that gave the cats something to chase and catch. Even now, though the cats are four years old, they still seem to enjoy this kind of activity.

Jim Yoakum's bobcat was about as tame as any of them get. Yet, I know of two different people who were bitten by him, though not seriously. They had tried to pet him and the cat thought they were trying to hold him. Jim himself was usually well decorated with scratches he suffered in handling or playing with the animal.

Bobcats make interesting, if somewhat unpredictable, pets, but most of them have a tendency to get more independent and more dangerous as they grow older. Some owners have resorted to defanging and declawing their pets. Ricci had very little trouble with his three (there were originally four until a stray dog got hold of one) while they were small and allowed to run free. Then, as they grew older and showed a tendency to extend their travels, he had to confine them. This had some effect on their temperament. One day they escaped from their pen and were gone for a week. They came back, however, but were watched more closely after that. One escaped again some months later and was killed by a motor vehicle on a nearby highway.

Regarding the unpredictability of bobcats, especially mature ones, Fred Painter relates what happened with two he had after he had given each a freshly killed pine squirrel. Though each had a squirrel, they started to fight over them, and Painter finally had to douse them with a bucket of water to separate them. After that, they were never again quite as friendly to each other or to people.

One of these bobcats died shortly thereafter from what Painter said was distemper, though this was not confirmed by autopsy. The other one, a female, lived to be eight years old and then died of a similar ailment. During the time he had this bobcat, Painter says that his wife could handle her very well but that he and the cat did not get along.

Painter reports that bobcats have violent tempers and, once upset, take some time to calm down. Several times both Fred and Mrs. Painter were bitten when their bobcat got excited or unduly disturbed about something.

There appears to be some mystery surrounding the relationship of bobcats not in family groups. It seems fairly well established that older and larger bobcats like to travel alone, yet there are reports from presumably competent observers of bobcats traveling in "droves." However, according to the literature, and the eyewitness reports I have received, bobcats (other than during the breeding season), when more than one are traveling together, are usually a family, either of half-grown kittens or of kittens with their mother.

A friend told me of a meeting with four young bobcats on a deer-hunting trip. He was slipping along the tops of a rimrock on a butte one fall day, hoping to surprise one of the big desert mule deer bucks that like to bed down in such places. He stepped over a narrow crevice and suddenly four young bobcats boiled out of the crevice snarling and hissing. They bounded off down the butte and disappeared.

54

Summer

Just recently, another friend, Dr. Jack McCarthy of Bend, Oregon, told me of an adventure with bobcats that not only was revealing of a bobcat's nature but showed some traits for which I can find no explanation.

He and a friend were hunting elk. While driving the back-country roads one morning, they rounded a bend and surprised a female bobcat and three kittens drinking from a puddle of water in the road. The female and two of the young disappeared into the underbrush at the side of the road, while the third kitten, seemingly confused, ran to the other side of the road and climbed a small tree.

Dr. McCarthy decided to climb the tree to see if he could capture the youngster. It was probably four or five months old and about the size of a large domestic cat. However, after he got up into the tree and close enough to get a good look at the animal, he decided that trying to capture this one with his bare hands was not a good idea. Next, he decided to push it out of the tree with a stick, in hopes that it would then run off and rejoin the rest of the family. He succeeded in pushing the cat out of the tree, and it alighted on its feet on the ground. The cat ran back toward the road, went under their car, and took refuge on top of a rear spring. They tried to get it out of there by poking at it with the stick, but it refused to move.

Finally, they started the car and drove down the road about three miles to a ranch owned by a friend. The cat stayed on the spring all the way and when they parked in the ranch yard, the cat was still there and refused to move. With a noose made from wire, they managed to drag the reluctant bobcat from under the car, and promptly up-ended a bucket over the animal. In the struggle the wire noose became quite tight around the bobcat's neck and McCarthy's companion, Bud Stipe, decided it should be loosened. He slowly eased his hand under the bucket and very carefully eased off the wire loop. During this process the cat remained perfectly still and made no attempt to harm him. Normally, one could have expected a severe

55

Bobcats have favorite vantage points.

scratching, but why the cat permitted itself to be handled without harming Stipe is something I can not explain. Perhaps the cat realized that it was being helped.

I mentioned earlier that adult bobcats seem to prefer being alone, but Sam Shaver told me of an experience that contradicts this idea. In visiting his traps one morning in late December, he came upon a spot where he had only a single trap set, but saw two bobcats there. Guessing as to which one was not in the trap, Shaver shot it, and his guess was correct. He then came in closer and disposed of the second cat. From his investigation, it appeared that one cat had been in the trap for four or five days and that the other animal had been there

56

most of the time. Rabbit fur and quail feathers scattered about indicated that the free one had been bringing the other one food during this time. Both were females, which rules out the possibility that they may have been mates. Possibly they were members of the same litter that stayed together longer than usual. Shaver estimated them to be at least a couple of years old and of about the same weight—around 25 pounds.

Bobcats in general are severe with domestic cats. In some remotely located ranches, domestic cats, introduced to help keep down the population of rats and mice, fall prey to bobcats. However, this is useful, since domestic cats, especially those that have become semiwild, are heavy predators on game birds. Thus, bobcat predation on domestic cats can be helpful to game species.

As I previously mentioned, I am familiar with only one instance in which bobcats and domestic cats got along: the tame bobcat and the domestic cat owned by Fred Painter. However, according to Painter, this was an exception made by the bobcat, who otherwise seemed always ready to dispose of any strange domestic cat.

A bobcat does not seem to be very particular about what he eats, just as long as it is meat. Examination of bobcat stomach contents has revealed such items as birds, snakes, and lizards. Even turtles, grasshoppers, and beetles occasionally form a part of its diet.

The determining factor, if there is any, of what a bobcat eats seems to be availability. Bobcats investigate almost everything that constitutes a potential meal. Rabbits or hares are their most abundant prey, and in all localities where studies of bobcat foods have been made, rabbit or hare represents the major part of the diet.

A full-grown rabbit is just about the right size to make a meal for a bobcat. Small rodents—mice, rats, and ground squirrels, for example—merely seem to whet a bobcat's appetite, and it takes considerable hunting to make a meal from mice.

When a bobcat kills more than it can consume, it often caches the

The World of the Bobcat

uneaten kill and returns to feed on it later. Generally, the bobcat partially covers the food with debris.

Variations will naturally occur in bobcat menus at different times of the year as availability of food varies. Deer meat forms a rather high percentage of bobcat food, and, as might be expected, this becomes most noticeable during the winter. While bobcats can and do kill deer, it seems to be generally believed that many of the deer they eat represent carrion. Animals wounded and lost by hunters, along with those that die of disease or winter starvation, provide most of the deer meat for bobcats. In some areas, where cougars are comparatively plentiful, their left-over deer kills also provide a food source for wandering bobcats.

Bobcat prey in the West: yellow-bellied marmot.

Jack rabbit, a favorite bobcat food.

Close shot of a sage grouse.

Bobcat prey: sage grouse. A male at left, struts before females.

Bobcat prey: pine squirrel, or red squirrel.

Bobcat prey: cottontail rabbit.

Bobcat prey: porcupine.

Bobcat prey: Oregon ground squirrel.

The World of the Bobcat

Porcupine has proved to be an important food for bobcats in Nevada, Utah, Vermont, Minnesota, Michigan, South Dakota, and Idaho. Sam Shaver observed that carcasses of accidentally trapped porcupines were readily eaten by other animals when lying belly-side-up, with no danger from the quills, whereas those with backs up weren't touched. Both coyotes and bobcats probably eat them under such conditions.

Oddly enough, porcupine quills, at least in a bobcat's body, seem to have little effect. Shaver has examined a number of bobcats with quills just under the skin of the neck and body. All have been quite soft, as if partially decayed. Richard Lee Weaver, in a report on bobcats and gray foxes attacking porcupines, stated: "In the case of the cats, quills had lodged much the same places...but were located lengthwise under the skin and were in a softened condition. None could be found in the body cavities. The extensive scar tissue around some of the quills indicated that they must have been there a long time."

In Minnesota, two biologists, D. S. Balser and John B. Moyle, found that "the bobcat feeds mainly on snowshoe hares and small mammals, but eats deer carrion if they can find it and may even kill deer if the opportunity arises."

Gashwiler and his colleagues expressed particular interest in finding bobcat meat as a food item in a bobcat's stomach. Evidence was sufficient to indicate that this may have been a case of cannibalism. I know of no other reports of such findings, which indicates that cannibalism is extremely rare.

Although bobcats are meat eaters, vegetable matter and plant foods are found in bobcat stomachs often enough and in sufficient quantities to indicate that these are eaten intentionally, probably as an aid to digestion, or for other therapeutic qualities.

While foods appear to follow a similar pattern throughout the bobcats' range, there are regional differences in food habits, since certain kinds of prey are not found in all areas. Livestock forms only a small part of the bobcat's diet, and that mostly sheep and goats. Swine comprise a small part of the food of bobcats in Florida, Georgia, and Louisiana.

Bobcats appear to feed on any small mammal that is available and easy to catch. These include, in addition to those already mentioned, shrews, moles, opossums, raccoons, skunks, house mice, mountain beaver, wood rats, meadow mice, cotton rats, deer mice, red-backed mice, harvest mice, muskrats, pine mice, rice rats, ground squirrels, tree squirrels, chipmunks, flying squirrels, prairie dogs, marmots, kangaroo rats, pocket mice, and pocket gophers.

Although bobcats prey upon both large and small birds, these represent only a small percent of their diet. Quail, ruffed grouse, sage grouse, blue grouse, sharp-tailed grouse, doves, and wild turkeys have been found in bobcat stomachs. Only a trace of aquatic game birds has been found. The non-game-bird species include sparrows, thrushes, flickers, jays, blackbirds, owls, hawks, and wrens.

Ernest Thompson Seton wrote that in sultry weather bobcats follow the dry beds of streams to pick up the catfish, crayfish, and frogs that remain in deep holes. While this agrees with what seems to be a typical feline preference for fish, especially in domestic cats, there is little corroboration from stomach analyses for the fact that bobcats eat fish. There are reports from Florida of their subsisting on a diet of crayfish and other crustaceans.

A bobcat will feed on any livestock and poultry, but appears to shy away from them except in an emergency, particularly because this puts him closer to man than he cares to be.

Autumn

LIKE MOST WILD ANIMALS, bobcats grow a thick, warm coat of fur for the cold winter weather and lose it in the summer. Observation of this molt and regrowth of the bobcat's coat in the wild is difficult, if not impossible. However, Jim Ricci keeps his two pet bobcats outside all of the time, so that changes in their pelage occur more or less naturally. Consequently, his observations of changes in the fur of his bobcats are relevant to what actually occurs in the wild. In other sections of the United States, the extent and the time of the changes are affected by climatic variations in the different areas.

Although Ricci made no record of when shedding was first noted, it is his recollection that the spring molt usually begins in March. This coincides pretty much with the end of extreme cold weather in central Oregon. Shedding of the winter coat is not accomplished gracefully. Instead, the hair comes out in chunks, leaving the bobcat looking ragged and unkempt. By summer, molting is complete and the resulting change in the animal's appearance is quite pronounced. The color of the fur is much lighter, almost a solid buff, and the black markings are not so much in evidence. The cats look much thinner and, according to Ricci, their appetites fall off considerably and they eat a great deal less in the summer months.

Late in the summer, nights grow colder and by September, there are frosts in the northern parts of the United States and in southern Canada. Along about this time the bobcat's appetite picks up. This

64

A bobcat in its thinner summer coat.

A bobcat in its shaggier winter coat.

probably coincides with the bodily needs of the cats in growing their winter coats. Regrowth is a gradual process, which, Ricci says, you hardly notice until suddenly, in October, you realize that the bobcats are fat and sleek and fully furred again.

Bobcats usually look much heavier than they actually are. Almost always, the observer will guess their weight at about 10 pounds more that it is. Partly, this can be attributed to the rangy build of a bobcat and its comparatively long legs. A 25-pound bobcat held up by its legs will be about 4 feet long.

The average weight of a mature bobcat is between 18 and 25 pounds. The male is generally larger than the female, and males up to 30 or 35 pounds are not uncommon. Ricci's two cats, both males, weighed 30 and 32 pounds in the fall of 1962, at which time they were in their fourth year. Stanley Young lists a bobcat of 69 pounds that was killed in Colorado in 1951. This was a monster when one considers that it was about three times a bobcat's average weight. Other large bobcats reported by Young include one of 59 pounds and one of 58½ pounds, both from Nevada; one of 55 pounds from New Hampshire, another 55-pounder from Ohio (killed in 1949), and one of 56 pounds from New Mexico. All of these extremely large bobcats were males.

The largest bobcat I have seen was taken on a central Oregon hunt with hounds, and weighed 35 pounds. Another caught on a similar hunt looked so large that I was sure he would weigh at least 35 pounds. When we got back to town and weighed him, he just topped 26 pounds. Bobcats in captivity have a tendency to be heavier, since they don't work off any excess weight hunting for food.

An average-size bobcat will be 33 to 43 inches in length. Tail length will be from 5 to 7 inches, although there seems to be considerable variation. For example, Young told of a 20-pound Mississippi bobcat with 4½-inch tail, while in Louisiana, a 20-pound bobcat had a 7-inch tail. The Mississippi bobcat had a body length of 34 inches;

A bobcat at bay on a pile of lava rock.

Bobcats are curious, and almost any movement attracts their attention.

the Louisiana cat, 33 inches. An Arkansas bobcat of the same weight also had a 7-inch tail but a 41-inch body length.

A bobcat's feet are large in comparison with those of domestic cats, though not as large as the feet of the Canada lynx. Its claws are retractable and, consequently, no claw marks appear in the tracks, which show four toe marks and a separate heel-pad mark. Footprints will be approximately 2 inches long by 1¾ inches wide, but may go up to 2¼ inches by 2 inches.

Joseph Grinnell and his coauthors in California describe a bobcat's foot as follows: "The end of the claw is tapered to a sharp point. The whole structure is admirably adapted to its function of forceful piercing and tearing, and protected against breakage. The claws are almost as important as the teeth."

The hind foot of a bobcat. *The front foot of a bobcat.*

Autumn

When walking at its normal pace, a wildcat will generally place each hind foot in the treads of the front one, which makes its snow trail seem as if it had traveled only on two feet. When the bobcat is walking or stalking prey, the tracks will be from 8 to 10 inches apart; at an easy trot, from 10 to 12 inches. Oddly enough, should a second or third bobcat be following along, it will quite likely step in the footprints of the first. Thus the trail will look as though only one bobcat has passed by.

Little is known about the lifespan of a bobcat in the wild. Having practically no enemies other than man, a bobcat would under normal conditions live until it became too old to feed itself and died from starvation or malnutrition. The general opinion seems to be that bobcats live from ten to fourteen years. However, bobcats in captivity,

The front foot, with claws extended.

Bobcat tracks in fresh snow.

Bobcat tracks in snow. Note "lone-foot effect" because the hind feet are set down exactly in the trail made by the forefeet. The tracks at the top of the picture are rabbit tracks.

not faced with the necessity of obtaining their own food, have lived longer. T. Donald Carter, a New Jersey naturalist, reported a male bobcat that lived in captivity for more than twenty-five years. This is very unusual.

When a mature bobcat glides noiselessly from its rocky cave or brushy windfall and moves into the approaching gloom of night for the evening's hunt, it has little to fear other than a chance encounter with man. A mature bobcat has substantially no natural enemies. There is reason to believe that the larger cougar may kill a bobcat if the two happen to meet. However, the scarcity of the cougar in general, and its absence over much of the bobcat's range, rules it out as a serious threat.

Coyotes, the most plentiful carnivores, apparently pose little danger to the bobcat. Under normal circumstances, it is doubtful that

A bobcat walking through snow.

A bobcat coming out of a resting place preparatory to hunting.

a coyote would have a chance against a bobcat. Razor-edged claws of the bobcat, propelled by its powerful hind legs, plus its strong jaws and sharp teeth, give it powerful instruments for both offense and defense. A trapper once told me that, as a defensive maneuver, the bobcat goes on its back, grasps its assailant with its front paws, and then rakes its victim's unprotected underside. Not many animals will recover from that kind of treatment. Operating as a pack, several coyotes might kill a bobcat, but there seems to be no record of it.

One animal that bobcats seem to leave entirely alone, though it appears to be no threat, is the badger. A badger is a fierce fighter, and though he has digging, rather than fighting, claws, he has a set of teeth like a barracuda's. It is probable that bobcats and badgers have sufficient respect for each other's fighting ability to go their separate ways.

Young bobcats may, at times, fall prey to predators, but this is

Autumn

rare. During their completely helpless periods they are in the protection of the dens. Later, as they move out into the open and learn to hunt, the female convoys them.

Man has little reason to fear a bobcat, though they occasionally attack people. However, this is a rare occurrence, and in all the cases with which I am familiar, the attacks were caused by some unusual circumstance. A cornered bobcat will fight anything, and there are recorded instances of females attacking men to protect their young. Rabid bobcats have been known to attack, and hunters using predator calls have suffered attacks when the bobcat got so close to what it thought was an easy meal that its attack was practically unavoidable. However, bobcats will generally seek safety in flight rather than get

Bobcats share their western range with coyotes, and there appears to be little conflict between the two.

involved with a human being. Even females, on occasion, abandon their young when man approaches, rather than stay and fight.

In order to get pictures of bobcats, I have climbed after them when they have been treed by hounds. It is often necessary to get within five or six feet of the animals to photograph them. Nevertheless, I have yet to have one take a swipe at me. Usually, they move away as far as they can without falling out of the tree and wait for whatever is going to happen.

A friend in central Oregon told me of witnessing an attack on his cocker spaniel by a bobcat. It happened during the summer while my friend was acting as a fire lookout on top of Black Butte. The cocker spaniel was playing at the base of the lookout tower when the bobcat came out of the brush and started chasing the dog. A shout from above scared the animal back into the brush. A short time later the cat was back and took up the chase again. This time he was stopped by a rifle bullet.

I have been attacked by a buck mule deer and by a bull elk during the rutting season, when my photographic enthusiasm put me closer to the animals than they thought I should have been. On one occasion, an irate badger, which I thought would be an easy subject, chased me up a high tree stump, then made its escape. All of which is merely an indication that nearly all wild animals can be dangerous, even one ordinarily as mild as a deer. I feel much safer in a tree with a bobcat than I do on foot around a rutting buck deer and his harem.

Though I have described a bobcat as a stealthy animal that slips silently through dense cover to avoid being seen, it can, when the occasion demands, run like a race horse.

One day I watched a mature bobcat streak across the desert with a half-dozen hounds no more than 50 yards behind. How fast it was going I could only guess, but it was moving fast enough to stay ahead of the hounds for a long way. Then it climbed a juniper tree.

In hunting bobcats with hounds, the chase usually follows a more

Treed bobcats.

The World of the Bobcat

or less standard pattern. The dogs are put on a bobcat's trail, which, if they take it readily, may be as much as several hours old. There follows a period of slow trailing by the dogs and then the quarry is jumped from its resting place. There follows a fast but comparatively short run before the cat takes to a tree.

The cat on the ground is able to outrun the dogs with an initial burst of speed, but is unable to maintain it. He's a sprint runner, not a long-distance runner. Even if he could outrun the dogs, a bobcat feels safer in a tree. At least this is true of northern bobcats. Southern bobcats do not take to trees quite so readily.

During times of food shortages bobcats extend their hunting territory. In a study made by Weldon B. Robinson and Eugene F. Grand from 1954 to 1957, 81 bobcats were captured, tagged, and released. Seven were recaptured and released again. Of the 48 recoveries, 17 were within 1 airline mile of the release points, 38 were within 5 miles and 44 within a 10-mile radius. Maximum movement was 23 miles.

Clair T. Rollings points out that, on five different occasions,

A desert bobcat in winter.

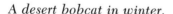

Autumn

Minnesota bobcats were tracked from one night's rest shelter to the next night's rest shelter. The distance traveled by the animals was from 3 to 7 miles, with an average of 5½ miles. In a straight line from rest shelter to rest shelter, however, the distance was only ¾ mile for the shortest and 3¾ miles for the longest.

A bobcat hunts by sight and sound rather than by scent, and darkness presents no problem. With the coming of night, the bobcat rises from its daytime shelter. Chances are it will stretch and yawn much as a domestic cat does and then start on the night's unhurried hunt. While a bobcat's hunting tactics are seemingly without plan, it frequents places where the type of small rodents it likes are apt to be and where, probably, it has fed before.

On velvet paws, the bobcat moves slowly through the darkness, taking advantage of irregularities in the terrain and stopping often to look and listen. It steals cautiously up to a vantage point and carefully looks over the cover ahead before moving on. Searching through thickets, it investigates the bushy tops of wind-felled trees. Rock piles and similar spots get a thorough going-over; it looks ahead, watchful

The World of the Bobcat

for the slightest movement that might mean food. Anything unusual gets prompt attention, for bobcats are notoriously curious.

A bobcat hunts by sight and sound rather than by scent, and its nightly wanderings may involve 4 or 5 miles of travel, yet it may remain only a short distance from where it started.

When the bobcat finally sights a potential meal, it stalks it carefully, creeping forward slowly, taking advantage of every bit of cover. When it is close enough, it charges with one or two quick leaps. If the attack fails, it will follow its prey only a short distance before abandoning the chase and searching for something easier.

Sometimes a bobcat hunts by patiently waiting atop a log, stump, rocky ledge, or some other favorite vantage point, until its prey chances to pass within range of a few short leaps. It has been reported that

A hunting bobcat investigates everything that moves.

This cat is getting ready to go up a tree.

Hunting in a rock pile.

A bobcat leaping from tree.

Autumn

leaps of 7 and 8 feet are not uncommon and, at times, a bobcat will cover 10 feet in a single bound.

M. A. Marston, reporting on winter hunting habits of bobcats in Maine, writes that "it appears frequently that a bobcat starting on a night hunt will often first spend some time trying to catch a snowshoe hare, hunting carefully through thickets and occasionally working up close enough to pounce. I did not see where a cat had killed a hare, though tracks were found several times which showed where one had leaped and missed its prey. In several instances the tracks showed that the cat had stopped hunting hares after failing in one or two attempts

Bobcats can take advantage of each tiny bit of cover.

Crouching in the snow ready
to leap on a prey animal.

Leaping bobcat.

The attack leap of a bobcat.
Note the extended claws.

From a vantage point atop a rock pile, a cat waits for a "meal" to go by.

and proceeded to deer yards either to hunt deer or to feed from a previously killed carcass."

From these observations one gets the idea that a bobcat prefers freshly killed meat and that it would much rather tackle a rabbit than the larger and more difficult deer.

From most of the reportings, it appears that when a bobcat decides to go after something as large as deer, it prefers to attack the animal while it is lying in its bed or to drop on its back from some high vantage point. In either case, this gives the cat a chance at a deer's vulnerable neck area without being in danger from the sharp hoofs which are a deer's best weapon.

Attacks on deer by bobcats are not always successful. Sometimes the intended quarry has sufficient warning to get the jump on the cat and make its escape. The bobcat usually does not pursue for very long.

83

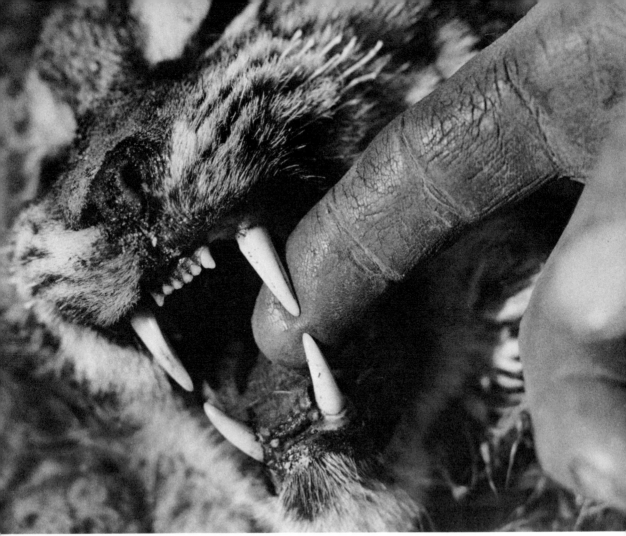

The carnassial teeth, longer and larger than the adjacent teeth, are adapted for cutting and shearing the prey. They are also wicked weapons of defense.

At other times, the cat may be unsuccessful in getting a firm grip on the animal and will fall off or be knocked off when the deer runs under heavy, low-hanging branches or through a patch of thick brush.

When a bobcat is successful in its attack, it fastens its relatively long canine teeth into the deer's neck, piercing the jugular vein or possibly reaching the spinal cord. The animal will often succumb immediately. When death does not come to the deer quickly, it will sometimes carry the bobcat for some distance on its back. It may have been observations of this kind that prompted the stories told by early

84

A young bobcat sharpening his claws.

explorers about bobcats riding through the woods on the backs of full-grown deer, sucking the blood of their victims.

The canine teeth of a bobcat are formidable weapons. I once compared those of a 30-pound bobcat with the canine teeth of a 150-pound cougar. While the cougar's canines were larger in circumference, the bobcat's were just as long and seemed much sharper. This may have been due to their stiletto-like appearance; nevertheless, it was obvious that the bite of a bobcat would penetrate just as deeply as that of a cougar. The cat family in general is the most highly specialized of all mammals for eating flesh. Their well-developed canine teeth are long and sharp and backed up by powerful jaws. The carnassials (teeth adapted for tearing flesh) have extreme development in the order Carnivora, and the molars in back of them are lost or reduced to vestiges.

Here is a hunting bobcat as described by Harold E. Anthony: "It was sneaking through the scattering of greasewood bushes flat upon its belly, its short tail twitching nervously . . . the cat took advantage

85

of every bush, stopping in the cover of each for a few moments."

Unlike the coyote, a bobcat makes no attempt to dig into the home of its intended quarry. A kangaroo rat or a ground squirrel that gets to its underground den is safe—at least for the time being. A bobcat's feet with their retractable claws are not adapted to digging.

Although bobcats are good climbers, they spend little time hunting in trees for food. A bobcat, being somewhat an opportunist, will eat almost anything in the way of meat, but generally picks the easiest obtainable. Birds and squirrels in trees are probably not the easiest things in the world for a bobcat to catch.

Some years ago, a predator control man for the Oregon State Game Commission and I put up a bobcat in a slide of enormous rocks on the rim of Crooked River Canyon in central Oregon. The cat was fairly stuffed with quail that had been wintering on a nearby ranch. There were thousands of these birds gathered in a small area. Since several inches of snow covered what natural foods there were, the quail fed from haystacks around the ranch. Surplus birds were being trapped by biologists of the State Game Commission and relocated in areas not so crowded. The bobcat was not only taking advantage of a more or less natural winter concentration but went so far as to wait until the trap was loaded, and then fed on the trapped birds. When the predator control man spotted the tracks and saw the feathers and other signs around his empty trap, he called his hounds and we went after the cat. The hounds were put on fresh tracks a quarter of a mile away from the quail trap, and the dogs were barking "treed" deep down in the rock slide 150 yards away in a matter of minutes. The bobcat, stuffed with quail, had headed for the nearest rock pile and holed up for the day.

After satisfying its hunger, a bobcat curls up in some nearby spot that gives it the protective cover it desires. It seems to attach no special significance to any particular shelter, preferring rather to take one close at hand. This fits the bobcat's role as an opportunist.

86

Winter

WE HAVE SEEN that bobcats will eat any game bird or animal they can get. At one time or another, analysis of the contents of bobcat stomachs and the study of carcasses of larger game animals found dead in the field have revealed that many species have been part of a bobcat's diet.

Antelope are occasionally killed by bobcats, but this is not common. The wide-open country preferred by antelope does not provide enough brush and rocky cover to suit the cats. Moreover, the eyesight of an antelope is comparable to man's as assisted by 8-power binoculars. Consequently, a bobcat might have great difficulty in stalking antelope without being seen. Obviously, a bobcat could never catch a running antelope, the fastest animal in the United States. Nevertheless, bobcats have killed antelope and such kills have not been limited to young animals.

Bobcats have been known to kill mature antelope such as these.

Mature deer, under this kind of winter conditions, are not difficult for a bob-cat to handle.

In my part of central Oregon, deer live in all sections where bobcats live. In fact, one of the hazards faced by bobcat hunters with hounds not thoroughly trained is that they often are sidetracked by deer and leave a cat track to follow that of a deer. The desert sections of central Oregon have their resident deer populations, and with the coming of winter, when the snows pile up in the high country, other deer migrate into this lower desert area, where they feed on sage and other browse during the winter.

Bobcats kill deer during any season of the year, but the largest numbers are taken during the winter, when other foods become scarce and deer "yard up" on account of the weather. While large deer are frequently killed by bobcats, most of the deer are small — under

88

Most deer killed by bobcats are of this size: a seven- to nine-month-old animal weighing under 100 pounds.

100 pounds. However, deer kills by bobcats are by no means limited to northern areas, where snow is a factor in making the deer more defenseless. There are a number of recorded deer kills in the South and the Southwest.

The availability of other food, principally rabbits, in a given area appears to have considerable limiting effect on the extent of deer kills by bobcats. While such predation is not exactly a rarity in Oregon, it does not seem to present much of a problem. This may be due to the fact that wintering areas for deer are more or less open desert, where snows are not too frequent or too deep and where there is a fair population of jack rabbits.

Marston, in his report on the winter relations of bobcats and

89

white-tailed deer in Maine, states: "The facts indicate that cats can take deer as they come and are able to kill one as easily as another provided they can approach near enough to make the attack." He further states: "Bobcats undoubtedly waste considerable meat when they kill a deer, as carcasses are found with varying amounts of meat remaining." As a possible reason for this, he suggests that bobcats find frozen meat difficult to eat and that, also, they find carrion distasteful.

Wild turkeys seem to be a favorite of bobcats in wild-turkey country. Stanley Young relates a reported eyewitness account of a bobcat catching a turkey on the ground. Wild turkeys have great ability to slip silently and unseen through the woods. They have keen hearing and eyesight, but if any predator is a match for them, it is no doubt, the bobcat. I have been unable to find any record of bobcat attacks on turkeys roosting in trees, but it seems a logical way to hunt them. Small birds roosting on the outermost branches of a tree might be difficult for a bobcat to reach, but turkeys, weighing upward of 10 pounds, would have to roost in closer to the tree trunks and would be accessible to a marauding cat.

Ernest Thompson Seton reports that, in 1920, turkey populations had declined materially in Arkansas until higher prices on bobcat

In the West, valley quail are a favorite food of bobcats.

fur stimulated trappers into going after them. Thereafter, turkey populations increased. H. J. Nichols, veteran Florida bobcat hunter, remarked that wherever there was a bunch of wild turkeys, you could depend on finding several cats in the vicinity.

There have been a great many stories of bobcat predation on domestic livestock recorded and documented over the years. Taken altogether, this means that a bobcat will feed on any domestic animal it is capable of subduing. However, on further analysis, it would seem that predation on domestic animals represents, for the most part, only a supplement to a bobcat's diet. Most bobcats still prefer to prey on wild birds and animals. Simply because domestic animals are plentiful does not necessarily mean that cats will kill them.

Trapper Sam Shaver once told me of getting a call from Jack Shumway, a local sheep rancher, who had been losing a lot of lambs to an unknown predator. It was early in the spring, a few days after lambing, and Shumway had turned the lambs and ewes out of the lambing pens into nearby pastures. For three nights in a row, something had gotten into the pasture and killed twenty-five to thirty lambs each night. According to Shaver, the dead lambs were strung across the field as though whatever had killed them had walked through the flock killing all those in its path just to have something to do. None of them had been eaten. The lambs had all been killed by a bite at the base of the skull, a typical bobcat attack. Shaver set his traps for bobcat, two days later, he had a big old tom bobcat. Shumway lost no more lambs.

There have been several cases involving such "blood-lust" kills. Although most of them involve sheep, chickens, turkeys, goats, and pigs also come in for considerable attention. A bobcat is able to steal pigs away from the sow simply by drawing the sow into an attack and then, with its agility and speed, grabbing the young ones before the sow can get back to protect them.

Not all stock predation represents a wholesale slaughter by bobcats. Often, a bobcat will prey on a nearby flock of sheep or chickens,

91

feeding on it according to the demands of its appetite until the supply is exhausted or it is captured.

It is predation on livestock that is primarily responsible for the need to control bobcat populations. Different methods of control have been tried from time to time with varying success. One of the oldest methods is the bounty system, which came into existence before the Revolutionary War. In 1962, only thirteen states were still paying bounties on bobcats. The majority consider the bounty system ineffective as a control measure.

The worst feature of the bounty system is that it has almost inevitably led to fraudulent practices. In some instances, it has actually resulted in an increase in populations of the bountied animal. This happens when the bounty hunter makes it a practice to free all females and only claim the bounty on males, thus ensuring a plentiful supply of predators for future bounties.

It was not uncommon for the necessary evidence for a bounty claim—hides, ears, paws, etc.,—to be brought in from a state that paid no bounties or that did not pay as much. Frequently, the hides of other species, such as ocelots or raccoons, were brought in and bountied as bobcats to officials who either didn't know or didn't care that the skins were not those of bobcats. All too often, bountying officials were in on the deception.

Bounties were also inadequate as a control measure because the bobcats killed were not necessarily the ones that were doing the most damage. Bounty hunters were much more interested in the numbers they could kill rather than in getting the predators that were killing game animals or domestic stock.

The control of predators is often necessary for the protection of livestock and wildlife, but these controls should be applied at the right time and place. Rarely do bobcats become a menace over a large area. More often than not, it is a single animal operating in a small area that causes the problem. It does no good to trap or kill a hundred bobcats in some isolated area, while the one or two that are causing the trouble remain free to continue their depredations.

The best control method at present seems to be trapping, done by a salaried trapper paid by state or federal government and available on call to handle predator problems as they come up. This is the way Sam Shaver operates. Most of his activities are based on calls from farmers and ranchers who are having troubles with bobcats or coyotes.

Steel traps are considered inhumane by many people, but as yet no humane and practical trap has been devised. Trappers are aware of this, and could something as effective but less cruel be developed, they would be glad to use it.

A trapped bobcat in a defensive position.

The World of the Bobcat

Effective bobcat trapping depends primarily on setting traps in the proper places. Consequently, a trapper is guided by evidence of a bobcat's presence such as tracks, scats, and scratches. There are several ways of setting traps, and probably each experienced trapper has his own favorites. Since they are basically much the same, I will describe one used in Oregon by Shaver, who is a second-generation professional bobcat and coyote trapper. Favorite trapping spots are on rimrocks and lava rock piles, along which he knows from the signs the bobcats are traveling. If a cat has been molesting livestock or deer, traps are placed near a carcass in anticipation that it will return to feed.

While handling the traps and making the set, Shaver wears gloves that have, through long usage, been fairly well saturated with a prepared scent lure, to eliminate human odor. This is the only time these gloves are worn. The traps are set to one side of the trail, generally as a single, but occasionally two traps are used. In setting the trap, enough dirt is scooped out to allow the trap to be set below ground level. Fine, dry dirt is sprinkled over the trap, care being taken that nothing gets under the pan that will prevent it from triggering the trap. Shaver then places a square of old canvas over the trap as a trap pad and covers the entire set with another sprinkling of dry dirt. By the time he's finished, the spot looks no different from its surroundings. Shaver always uses a scent, which is placed on a weed, rock, or similar object, some 6 to 8 inches from the trap. This is known as a "scent post" and is so termed because they are the kinds of places selected by bobcats for voiding urine or feces.

The traps are either fastened by chain to a steel stake buried in the ground or to a log or a downed branch as a drag. A drag is more favored because it gives under pressure and permits the trapped animal some movement, and the animal is not so apt to pull free from the trap.

Shaver told me about one such drag set that almost proved his undoing. The trap was set near a pile of lava rocks known locally as a

94

"lava boil." The area is liberally sprinkled with these formations, created a long, long time ago when hot lava flowed over much of this country. These rocks are usually honeycombed with passages and make fine hiding places for bobcats. He came by one morning to inspect the trap and noted that it was gone. As is his custom, he made a careful survey of the rocks and brush cover from a distance but was unable to spot the cat. A circle around the pile of rocks disclosed no trails leading away, so he was certain that the cat was hidden somewhere on the rock pile. With gun in hand, a .22-caliber pistol, he began a cautious examination of the brush-covered rocks. Suddenly, from its hiding place under some brush, the cat leaped at him. Shaver got off one quick shot and, though it hit the cat, it did not stop the animal from hooking its razor-sharp claws into Shaver's abdomen. Sam stumbled backward and the cat, held by the drag wedged in the rocks, could not follow. Shaver then finished off the cat and headed for town and medical attention. He had several severe lacerations on his abdomen which would have been much worse had he not been wearing a jacket at the time. He has the scars to remind him that cats when cornered can be dangerous.

Prepared scents are important in bobcat trapping. Decomposed fish is commonly used as a base, but this is often modified by the addition of other types of decomposed meat—the bladders of coyotes and bobcats and different kinds of animal fat. Oil of catnip is also frequently used with considerable success.

One of the most controversial methods of predator control is the use of poisoned baits. A great many people—sportsmen, naturalists, and conservationists—bitterly oppose the use of the highly developed poisons now available. Some of these are known to be effective through several carriers. For example, a poisoned coyote may eventually furnish a meal for magpies, which may then fly on to die far away and provide an effective poisoned-meat source for some other bird or animal miles from the original poisoned bait.

95

A bobcat treed by hounds.

Bobcats do not take poisoned baits readily. This may be due in part to a seeming reluctance of bobcats to eat carrion. Also, such baits do not attract cats readily, for their sense of smell is not as acute as that of the coyote.

Up to 1962, bobcats received practically no protection from game laws. Only one state had a closed season, and that was limited to a particular area of the state. Eleven states do not even require a bobcat hunter to purchase a hunting license. Others merely require that a person have a general hunting license, regardless of what he is after.

96

Eager hound scrambles part way up tree after bobcat.

Bobcat hunting is a rough sport, rewarded only by a trophy of the hunt—the bobcat's skin—and the bounty that may be on the animal. Until manufactured predator calls came into wide use a few years ago, the only successful way to hunt bobcats was with a pack of trained hounds.

Most of the sport in hunting bobcats is in listening to the hounds and watching them work. Quite often, hounds on a "hot trail" will quickly outdistance the hunters. The bobcat is seldom seen during the chase, and when it is over, he is usually perched high in a tree

97

with the dogs clamoring below. Killing the bobcat is anticlimactic. It requires no skill and presents no danger.

I think the real pleasure for the hunter in a bobcat chase and its successful conclusion is the knowledge that his trained dogs have out-smarted one of the cleverest animals in the country.

The techniques of hound hunting will vary somewhat in different parts of the country, as terrain and climate influence the animal's actions and escape tactics. In the Northwest and the Northeast, where much of the hunting is done during the winter when there is snow on the ground, fresh tracks are located and the hounds turned loose on them. In areas that don't have snow, a "strike" dog is allowed to run and the remainder of the pack kept on leashes until the strike dog announces that he's found fresh scent. The scent of a bobcat is appar-ently not as strong as that of a cougar, and it takes a fairly fresh bobcat track to interest the hounds.

All of my bobcat hunting has been done in central Oregon, where we never attempt to hunt without good tracking snow. This makes for tough walking when the snow is deep, and adds complications of its own as the snow alternately freezes and thaws. A light crust that will hold a bobcat won't hold dogs and man. At such times, the cat may simply walk out of the area and leave you exhausted somewhere on his back trail.

The first hunt I ever participated in was in big timber on the eastern slopes of the Cascades in central Oregon. There had been fresh snow the night before, and in drifts and hollows it was a foot and a half deep. The bobcat track we started on was fresh and the hounds took to it eagerly. We followed from eight in the morning till four in the afternoon, when the cat finally took cover in some crevice in a steep, rocky bluff. It was much too steep for either dogs or hunters to climb, and we had to give it up. How far we'd walked that day I have no idea. But it had been steady going, though far from being in a straight line, as we followed the cat's devious routes and circles. At

98

the end, we were 5 airline miles from our starting point and practically exhausted. Sometimes the chase is unbearably long and, at other times, unbelievably short.

The shortest I can remember was only 150 yards. Another time, we put the dogs on an early-morning track in 2 inches of fresh snow and were off on a fast run in some rolling, rocky hills called Powell Buttes. It was a clear day and a warm sun started melting the snow. The heat, the melting snow, and the tendency of the bobcat to cut across all the bare rock it could find kept us moving so slowly that we never could "warm up" the track and the cat got away. Later that same day on the way home, we spotted a fresh track in a muddy spot in the road. The dogs liked it and took off on the bobcat's trail under a full head of steam. They jumped the cat a couple of hundred yards off the road and quickly put it up a tree.

The best time to hunt in snow country seems to be early in the morning after a fresh snowfall of a few inches. This covers all the old tracks, and anything you see is bound to be fresh. Since bobcats do most of their hunting at night, such tracks will usually be from one that killed late and is heading for some resting place, or from one whose night hunting was unsuccessful and is still on the prowl. Obviously, any tracks one can find will be no older than the most recent snowfall — and the fresher the tracks, the better the chances are for success.

Wildcat hunting with hounds has long been a favorite sport in the southeastern part of the country. It appears that, in that section, bobcats do not tree as readily as they do in the North, and prefer to either outrun or outmaneuver the dogs on the ground. If they aren't able to do this, they will often stop and fight the dogs on the ground.

This characteristic of southern bobcats, plus the fact that much of the hunting covers terrain over which it is impossible for men to follow the dogs successfully, has resulted in two basic methods of hunting in that area. One is to turn the dogs loose and leave it up to them to either get the cat or let it get away. The other method is to place hunters on stands near strategic openings and hope that one of them will get a shot at the bobcat as the dogs push it across country. According to Harold E. Anthony, "The wildcat rarely trees, but usually, rabbit-like, runs round and round in a limited circle depending on outrunning or dodging the dogs."

This sort of maneuvering would give armed men on stands a fairly good chance of a shot at the animal.

H. J. Nichols, the Florida bobcat hunter, uses many more dogs than do hunters in the Northwest. On one of his recent successful bobcat excursions, there were seventeen hounds in the pack. The most I have seen in Oregon was five. However, one good hound is enough in open desert country, since the bobcats usually take to a tree or seek refuge in the rimrocks.

Mr. Nichols says they do not take a gun along on his bobcat-hunting trips. On those rare occasions when a cat does take to a big tree, they call off the dogs, leave the treed animal, and hunt for the trail of another.

Bobcats running ahead of hounds do not depend entirely on outrunning the dogs or on the possibility of getting into a tree as a means of escape. They know many tricks and seem to be adept at making up new ones. They don't run in a straight line, but rather tend to circle and to do some back-tracking to confuse the dogs. In central Oregon, they will climb a bare pile of rocks and move around there long enough to get the tracks pretty well jumbled. Often, when following hounds, we find them puzzling around on bare rocks, bawling aimlessly. It is then necessary to circle the rock pile, locate the outgoing tracks, and get the hounds started on the trail again.

In the South, a favorite means of escape for bobcats is through water. They will swim streams and lakes to lose the trailing dogs. As I mentioned earlier, one cat, while trying a lake escape, killed one of the dogs that tried to follow and was in turn killed when the other dogs caught up with it.

100

After treeing, the bobcat jumped from the high limb to the right in an effort
to confuse the dogs.

Highly productive bobcat country in central Oregon.

A favorite trick of central Oregon bobcats is to disappear into a crevice or a tunnel that is too small for a dog to enter.

On one hunt, the dogs took a fresh track and, no more than 500 yards from where they started, barked "treed." My hunting companions and I ran there and found the four hounds circling a small jack pine, bawling proudly. We walked around the tree and looked into its sparse, needle-covered branches. There was no cat there despite the assurance the hounds were giving us. We circled the tree again and found where the cat had leaped out, probably before the arrival of the dogs, and had bounded off. The dogs took to the tracks again and, 200 yards farther on, showed us where the cat had gone into a crack in

102

the lava rock. The entrance was too small for the dogs, and though we could hear the cat snarling inside, we had to abandon it.

Another time the dogs took off on a hot track that led straight across a stretch of open desert. There were no trees around for some distance and no noticeable rock piles. The way the dogs were acting, we were sure they were only seconds behind a cat, and fully expected they would put up the animal in the open, flat country. When we caught up with them a few minutes later, they were running in and out of a cave opening that went down under a layer of rock. One of the hunters crawled into this small cave but could see nothing because of darkness. The dogs would enter only so far and then, yelping their disappointment, come out again. It seemed obvious that the cat knew this place was there and that it could make its escape there whenever hard pressed.

A limiting factor to this kind of bobcat hunting is the necessity for a good pack of hounds. It is almost impossible to buy a *good*, well-trained bobcat hound, although it is not too difficult to find hound pups for sale with good potential. But this is no guarantee that the dog will make a cat hound, and there seems to be no way of telling except by going through a training period and trying one out.

Keeping a pack of hounds also presents a problem. Crowded residential sections do not take kindly to the deep-voiced baying of four or five hounds — it may sound pretty out in the country when the dogs are warming to a fresh track, but not to city residents.

Since a hound pack on a track is usually far ahead of the hunters and is thus out of their control, all sorts of things happen. Sometimes, if the hunters do not catch up, the dogs just keep going, and if they lose the track, they may pick up another before the hunters catch up. All of my bobcat-hunting friends have lost dogs from time to time. Sometimes a dog or two will straggle home after a few days, or some rancher 10 miles away from where they've been hunting will call in to tell them he has one of the dogs. Occasionally, one doesn't return

103

at all and no one knows what happened to it. If it happens to be an especially good dog, the loss is a severe one.

However, a hound pack is not the only means of hunting bobcats successfully. In recent years, the use of a predator call for hunting coyotes, foxes, and bobcats has become popular. Actually, it makes more of a sport out of bobcat hunting, I think, than the use of hounds.

A predator call usually imitates the squealing sound of a rabbit in distress. To predators, this sounds like an easy meal and they are attracted to it. According to most of the reports from users of these calls, coyotes and foxes answer in haste, but a bobcat, being more cautious, approaches the source of the sound carefully. Coyotes will often come in close, and I have heard of some instances where they have jumped on top of the caller. However, the hunters I have talked to who have killed bobcats by using calls say they have to be shot much farther away than a coyote, or they're apt to get suspicious and run off. Of all the predators that answer these calls, the bobcat is the hardest to fool and the hardest to get a shot at.

The hunter using a predator call must first locate an area that bobcats travel. Tracks and signs will indicate likely places. He should have a place to hide — one from which a large area is visible so that he can watch for any bobcats answering his call. He should be able to approach his chosen hiding place without exposing himself to the area he expects the bobcat to come from, and he should also take advantage of the wind. Some animals can smell man quite a distance away. Early morning and late evening are the best times for calling. If there's no answer to the call after about thirty minutes, the hunter should try another location.

The first time I tried a predator call was several years ago, shortly after the first commercial ones were put on the market. I was quite skeptical about their effectiveness and so made only a halfhearted, sloppy attempt at calling up a predator. I was sitting on a rock in a sand and sagebrush clearing, in full view of anything that might come

104

along. Fifty yards away was a long, low rimrock that was pretty well covered with scrubby juniper. I followed the directions that came with the patented call for about fifteen minutes and then, because nothing came running across the open toward me, decided it wasn't going to work. I got up to go and saw a flash of brown behind the junipers on the rimrock. It was an animal that had answered the call and had no doubt been sitting there behind the trees watching me. I might have seen it, had I had more confidence in the call. I checked along the rim and found the well-defined tracks of a mature bobcat leaving the area. It is quite likely that it had been resting in one of the rocky crevices near by when I started to call.

Most bobcat matings take place during the winter. However,

A bobcat in mid-leap.

there are indications that young bobcats may be born during any month of the year. This indicates that breeding also may take place in any month. However, most mating activity would appear to occur from February to May.

In the warmer parts of the country, breeding usually starts somewhat earlier in the year than in the North. Females not impregnated during the normal late-winter and spring season may come in heat later in the year. Males, however, are sexually active the year around.

It is during the breeding season that a bobcat is at its noisiest. The male may travel much farther than its normal hunting range during this period—up to a 20- or 25-mile circle in search of a mate. The caterwauling that accompanies the mating is much louder than that of domestic cats. In some instances, according to Young, "the sound has been recorded as reaching a mile."

Jim Ricci tells me that on several occasions, bobcats, apparently females in heat, have come near his two captive males in their outdoor pens and kept his whole family awake with noises sounding like a woman's scream.

Gashwiler reported the trapping of two adult female bobcats. A male was caught in the traps after each female. The condition of the females indicated that they were either breeding or in estrus. "Both animals had been chewed around the neck. The mating period is apparently a trying one for the females."

Jaeger reports an observation of bobcat mating as follows: "I was awakened near midnight by an interrupted series of ferocious hisses, shrill screams, harsh squalls, and deep-toned yowls. No alley strays could ever have half-equalled this cat concert of the desert wilds. Luckily, it was moonlight and I was able to see the animals almost perfectly. The female most of the time lay crouched upon the ground while the big male, which must have weighed twenty pounds, walked menacingly about her. Sometimes they both sat upright facing each other. The loud and ludicrous serenade was kept up for almost half an hour, and, it ended with a dual climax of discordant, frightening squalls as mating took place."

The gestation period for bobcats has been variously reported as from fifty to sixty days. Palmer states that the gestation period is sixty-three days or more.

Gashwiler and his colleagues obtained birth dates of thirteen litters, mostly from females that bore young while in traps. Bobcat births by months obtained in this manner showed:

Month	Litters
MARCH	1
APRIL	4
MAY	4
JUNE	1
JULY	3
	13

If a gestation period of sixty-three days is used in figuring backward from the birth of each litter, it would appear that mating started in January and ended in May, with the peak period being in February and March.

Conclusion

IN 1634, a writer of the time described bobcats in this manner: "The English kill many of these, accounting them very good meate. Their skinnes be a very deepe kind of Furre, spotted white and black on the belly."

Helenette Silver, writing of the history of New Hampshire game and furbearers, states: "Hare and rabbit were common when white men first came to this country, but this fact does not appear to have resulted in an abundance of either wildcats or lynx. They are scarcely mentioned in Colonial times, and local bounties were not offered."

However, Stanley Young writes that "Massachusetts, by 1727, placed a bounty of 20 shillings for every full-grown wildcat . . ." So apparently, the animals had become somewhat of a problem by then.

Lewis and Clark reported on bobcats in the lower Columbia River Basin and mentioned that it required four skins to make a robe. Indian tribes in that area apparently prized bobcat skins for robes very highly.

Records of fur transactions from this country's early days repeatedly mention bobcat and wildcat furs. Bone remains of wildcats have been found in Indian ruins over 2,000 years old, especially in the southwestern section of the United States. It is obvious that bobcats have been on this continent for quite a long time.

Oddly enough, however, it is quite likely that there are more bobcats now, at least in some areas, than ever before. For example, the number of bobcats bountied in Oregon from 1951 through 1960

108

Bobcats stay on the ground most of the time but will occasionally take to a tree to hunt or to escape danger.

increased from 1,357 in 1951 to 3,128 in 1959. In 1960, they dropped again to 2,263. It is interesting to note, in view of the above, that C. H. D. Clarke in his reports on population fluctuations gave cycles of about ten years for snowshoe hare, muskrat, lynx, and other furbearers.

Robert L. Patterson, in his book on the sage grouse in Wyoming, wrote that "it has been the opinion of the local agents of the Branch of Predator and Rodent Control that bobcat populations have increased quite widely in the state in recent years."

Pollack and Sheldon, in writing of bobcats in Massachusetts,

The World of the Bobcat

stated that there was much evidence that the bobcat is more abundant in that state than it was a hundred years ago. The probable cause, they surmised, was that a hundred years ago, 70 per cent or more of Massachusetts was farm land, whereas now some 75 per cent is in woods.

While it may reasonably be expected that an animal such as the bobcat would have gradually given way as the early pioneers moved westward, and more and more country was opened up to settlers, this does not seem to have been true. Although densely populated suburban areas and cities do not furnish home habitats for a bobcat, it has benefited from American civilization in a number of ways. Wildlife management, or encouragement, though aimed primarily at game birds and animals, has no doubt been a benefit to all wildlife.

The creation of additional farm lands through irrigation and reclamation has added thousands of acres to this country's grain lands. Rodents follow the grain, and bobcats follow the rodents. Given some brush or rocky cover and a reasonable food supply, a bobcat can survive.

With bobcat populations apparently either holding steady or increasing, the question of the economic value — good or bad — of the

Running through the sagebrush.

A year-old Oregon bobcat. Note white undertip of tail.

bobcat becomes important. It is known, of course, that bobcats do prey on game birds and animals and upon domestic livestock. Are the bobcat's depredations more costly than the value of the services it performs?

Since bobcat predation on deer seems to get the greatest amount of publicity, a comparison of the general-season deer kill in Oregon with the numbers of bobcats bountied should give some indication

111

of what effect, if any, bobcat populations have on the number of deer in the state.

Year	General Season Deer Kill	Bobcats Bountied
1951	57,000	1,357
1952	75,000	1,681
1953	105,000	1,464
1954	112,000	1,887
1955	131,000	2,786
1956	120,000	2,861
1957	115,000	2,809
1958	115,000	2,819
1959	144,000	3,128
1960	153,000	2,263

Beginning in 1952, controlled shooting of does was permitted, and in certain years subsequent to 1952, special limited-permit seasons were inaugurated in areas where deer were too concentrated. The number of deer killed during these special post-general-season hunts is not included in the above. Despite the steady increase in the number of deer harvested, the Oregon State Game Commission still considered the deer populations excessive and permitted doe shooting in 1962. The number of bobcats bountied indicates an increase in these animals, too, during the past several years. It seems fairly obvious that bobcat predation in Oregon has had no significant influence on the deer populations.

As W. Robert Eadie points out, "There is no good evidence that the toll of game taken by bobcats is a serious drain on wildlife populations. It is quite possible that they merely harvest a yearly surplus which would be removed by some other agency anyway.

Conclusion

"For Pennsylvania and Maine, there are data to show that bobcats kill deer, both adults and young. This is most frequent in winter . . . Since many of these regions have a surplus deer problem, the relatively small number taken by bobcats cannot be serious."

Evaluating the bobcat as a livestock predator is a somewhat different problem from evaluating its effect on wildlife. While the over-all predation of livestock may seem minor, it is never so to the farmer or rancher who has suffered the loss. Individual ranchers have sustained high losses from bobcat predation, even though their neighbors may have had no losses at all.

Earlier, I described the losses of one Oregon rancher who had more than seventy-five lambs killed by a single bobcat over a period of three nights. Entire flocks of poultry have been decimated in a single night. Hamilton records that "one Texas bobcat killed over $300 worth of Angora goats, and another in a month had killed on a single ranch, 53 rams, 1 ewe, and 1 goat."

In almost all of the instances where great domestic stock predation has taken place, it has been the work of especially destructive individuals, some of which have apparently become "killers" in the truest sense of the word, for they destroy far more than they can eat. In fact, it appears that often they do not kill to eat at all but just for the thrill, or savagery, of killing. However, bobcats in general should not be condemned for the misdeeds of a few.

According to Robert Eadie, "In 1920, the damage to domestic stock by each bobcat was estimated at fifty dollars a year, but this was not supported by definite data. The value of these cats in destroying destructive rodents must be subtracted from any damage done. In California it was concluded from food habits studies that 50% of the bobcat's food was beneficial to man's interests, 33% harmful, and 17% neutral. In Minnesota, the bobcat was considered beneficial. The predation on deer and grouse was regarded as negligible, and the take of varying hare, porcupine, and small rodents was considered

113

beneficial. In Massachusetts, the bobcat's assets as a game animal outweigh any damage it does to game populations."

It is also fairly well established that bobcats provide a worthwhile control on rodent populations and that in most instances the game birds and animals taken by bobcats are the weak and diseased ones whose removal actually benefits those that remain. However, there are other values to be taken into consideration with respect to bobcats. It is in many ways a highly admirable species of native fauna deserving of a permanent place in this country. If for no other reason, its ability to coexist with man without protection is indicative of its independence and abilities.

Besides its ecological value, or its place in nature in helping to suppress populations of rats, mice, ground squirrels, and other rodents, what values have bobcats to man?

For a great many years the value of the bobcat as a game animal has been admired by that small group of sportsmen who have had the hunting much to themselves. Undoubtedly, many others will join them in the future as the use of predator calls brings the sport to others. It may even reach the point where bobcats will be given the same protection as other game animals, although I doubt this. Any animal capable of striking back as the bobcat does is not as avidly hunted as the milder species. Another large segment of potential bobcat hunters will not bother because bobcats are not considered to be edible, as deer, grouse, and other so-called game animals are.

Actually, the bobcat is edible, but most reports indicate that the meat is of poor quality. Harold E. Anthony says, "Dr. C. Hart Merriam has eaten its flesh and pronounces it excellent. It is white, very tender, and suggests veal more than any other meat with which he is familiar."

This does not agree with the findings of two friends of mine who have eaten the animal. Ed Park, while acting as fire lookout one summer, killed a bobcat that was lingering near the lookout tower. Curious as to how it would taste, he cooked a hindquarter of the animal. Park

114

A bobcat treed by hounds.

reports that the flavor was not good, that it was very strong, or rank, and that his dog refused to eat it.

Sam Shaver told me he fed cooked bobcat meat to a couple of unsuspecting relatives and they didn't like it either. He also said it had an extremely strong, unpleasant odor while cooking.

Robert Eadie reports: "Local markets for carcasses exist in some areas, as in San Francisco, California, where the Chinese population seek this animal for medicinal purposes."

While, generally, the bobcat is of little value as a meat animal, it has always had some value as a furbearer. Indians used its fur for

115

The World of the Bobcat

robes and for other purposes. With the arrival of white trappers, the use of bobcat furs increased, but its fur has never achieved great value. In prime condition, it is a very soft fur, though not durable. Consequently, it has been most valuable as trimming for clothing. Victor Cahalane writes that the pelts make strong leather, but have rather brittle, perishable fur. R. E. Trippensee says that it has little value and does not take dye readily.

It is doubtful that bobcat fur will ever become valuable for use as wearing apparel. However, a tanned bobcat hide is decorative for

Lynx rufus fasciatus, *Northwestern bobcat.*

Conclusion

hanging in a den or a game room, as well as being an excellent trophy of a successful hunt.

Scientifically, the bobcat is classified in the phylum Chordata because it has a backbone, and as a mammal (Mammalia) because it is warm-blooded, has a four-chambered heart, hair on its body, gives birth to its young alive, and has mammary glands with which to nurse the young. It is of the order Carnivora because it is a flesh eater, and of the family Felidae, which includes cats and their allies. It is of the genus Lynx, which covers short-tailed cats. There are two species of that genus Lynx on this continent, *Lynx canadensis*, the Canada lynx, and *Lynx rufus*, the bobcat.

Lynx rufus pallescens, *pallid bobcat.*

The World of the Bobcat

The following information on races, or subspecies, of bobcats and their approximate range has been taken from Hall and Kelson's *Mammals of North America*.

Lynx rufus baileyi, Desert bobcat, or Bailey's bobcat. Range: Southeastern California, southern Utah, southern Nevada, southern and eastern Colorado, southwestern Nebraska, southwestern Oklahoma, western Kansas, western and northwestern Texas, New Mexico, Arizona, and northern Mexico.

Lynx rufus californicus, California bobcat. Range: Western California and north central California.

Lynx rufus escuinapae, Sinaloa bobcat. Range: South central Mexico.

Nova Scotia bobcat, Lynx rufus gigas. (Photo by Ken Gray, courtesy of Information and Education Division, Maine Department of Inland Fisheries and Game.)

Conclusion

Lynx rufus fasciatus, Northwestern bobcat. Range: Western Oregon, western Washington, southwestern British Columbia.

Lynx rufus floridanus, Florida bobcat. Range: Louisiana, except for northwest, eastern Arkansas, southeastern Missouri, western Kentucky, western Tennessee, central and eastern North Carolina, South Carolina, Georgia, Alabama, Mississippi, and Florida.

Lynx rufus gigas, Nova Scotia bobcat. Range: Maine, northern New Hampshire, northern Vermont, and southern Canada.

Lynx rufus pallescens, Pallid bobcat. Range: Eastern Washington, eastern Oregon, northeastern California, central and northern Nevada and Utah, northeastern and central Colorado, western Nebraska, western South Dakota, western North Dakota, Montana, Idaho, Wyoming, and southern Canada.

Florida bobcat, Lynx rufus floridanus. *(Photo courtesy of Florida Game and Fresh Water Fish Commission.)*

The World of the Bobcat

Lynx rufus peninsularis, Peninsular bobcat. Range: Baja California.

Lynx rufus rufus, Eastern bobcat. Range: Eastern North Dakota, eastern South Dakota, eastern Nebraska, eastern Kansas, eastern Oklahoma, western and central Arkansas, Missouri, Iowa, southern Wisconsin, southern Minnesota, Illinois, Ohio, Michigan, Indiana, Kentucky, central and eastern Tennessee, western North Carolina, western Virginia, West Virginia, Delaware, Pennsylvania, New Jersey, New York, southern New Hampshire, southern Vermont, Massachusetts, Connecticut, and Rhode Island.

Lynx rufus superiorensis, Lake Superior bobcat. Range: Northern Wisconsin, northern Minnesota, and southern Canada.

Lynx rufus texensis, Texas bobcat. Range: Central and eastern Texas, northwestern Louisiana, southwestern Oklahoma, and northeastern Mexico.

Almost as far back into the history of man as one can go, the members of the cat family have had a strange fascination for mankind. Cats have, in the past, been associated with witches and sorcerers. It is a cat, the African lion, that has for ages been known as the king of beasts. Another feline, the cheetah, has traditionally been a pet of Eastern monarchs and is also believed to be the fastest animal there is. This same fascination accrues to some extent to the bobcat.

The bobcat is an independent animal that asks but to be left alone. I have never seen one that had a look of fear in its eyes — even when caught in a steel trap or running for its life ahead of a pack of hounds. It is, to me, one of the most interesting species in this country. The bobcat will always fascinate me, if for no other reason, because of its inscrutability — no one will ever fully understand a bobcat.

Bibliography

Alberson, Haynes C., "Big Cat of Panasoffkee." *Florida Wildlife*, Vol. 6, No. 11 (April, 1953), pp. 22-24.

Amundson, R., "The Bobcat." *Wildlife of North Carolina*, Vol. 14, (December, 1950), pp. 4-7.

Bailey, Vernon, *The Mammals and Life Zones of Oregon.* U.S. Department of Agriculture, 1936.

Balser, D. S., and Moyle, John B., *Predators in Minnesota—Their Role and Control.* Minnesota Department of Conservation, 1958.

Benedict, John, "Wildcat Roundup." *Florida Wildlife*, Vol. 7, No. 8 (January, 1954), pp. 17, 32.

Blair, W. Frank, "The Mammals of a Florida Hammock." *Journal of Mammalogy*, 16:273 (1935).

Bodart, C., "Bobcat." *Outdoor Nebraska*, Vol. 32, No. 3 (Summer, 1954), p. 26.

Burr, J. G., "Fanged Fury." *Texas Game and Fish*, Vol. 6, No. 6 (May, 1948), pp. 4, 18.

Cahalane, Victor H., "King of Cats and His Court." *National Geographic*, Vol. LXXXIII, No. 2 (February, 1943), pp. 217-259.

———, *Mammals of North America.* New York, The Macmillan Company, 1947.

Bibliography

———, "Mammals of Chiricahua Mountains, Arizona." *Journal of Mammalogy,* 20:427 (1939).

Campbell, L., "Raising a Wildcat's Kittens." *Audubon Magazine,* Vol. 64, No. 4 (July-August, 1962), pp. 204-206.

Carter, T. Donald, "Remarkable Age Attained by Bobcat." *Journal of Mammalogy,* 36:291 (1955).

Clarke, C. H. D., "Fluctuations in Populations." *Journal of Mammalogy,* 30:23 (1949).

Compton, Horace O., "Effects of Predation on Pronghorn Antelope Numbers in South Central Oregon." Unpublished Master's thesis, Oregon State University, 1958.

Crane, Jocelyn, "Mammals of Hampshire County, Massachusetts." *Journal of Mammalogy,* 12:269 (1931).

Cross, R. H., Jr., "The Bobcat." *Virginia Wildlife,* Vol. 9, No. 3 (March, 1948), pp. 19-20.

Dill, Herbert H., "Bobcat Preys on Deer." *Journal of Mammalogy,* 28:36 (1947).

Eadie, W. Robert, *Animal Control in Field, Farm and Forest.* New York, The Macmillan Company, 1954.

Edminster, Frank C., *The Ruffed Grouse.* New York, The Macmillan Company, 1947.

Fox, Hope S., "The Bobcat." *Nature Magazine,* Vol. 49, No. 2 (February, 1956), pp. 69-72.

Gashwiler, Jay S., Robinette, W. Leslie, and Morris, Owen W., "Breeding Habits of Bobcats in Utah." *Journal of Mammalogy,* 42:76 (1961).

———, "Food of Bobcats in Utah and Eastern Nevada." *The Journal of Wildlife Management,* 24:226 (1960).

122

Bibliography

Grinnell, Joseph, Dixon, Joseph, and Linsdale, Jean M., *Fur Bearing Mammals of California*. Berkeley, University of California, 1937.

✗Hall, E. Raymond, and Kelson, Keith R., *Mammals of North America*. New York, The Ronald Press Company, 1959.

Halloran, Arthur F., "Carnivores of San Andres Mountains, New Mexico." *Journal of Mammalogy*, 27:161 (1946).

Hamilton, W. J., Jr., *American Mammals*. New York, McGraw-Hill Book Company, Inc., 1939.

————, *The Mammals of the Eastern United States*. Ithaca, N.Y. Comstock Publishing Company, 1943.

Hansen, G. H., "Predator Control." *Oregon State Game Commission Bulletin*, Vol. 9, No. 11 (November, 1954), pp. 3-4.

Ingles, Lloyd Glenn, *Mammals of California and Its Coastal Waters*. Stanford, Calif., Stanford University Press, 1946.

Jaeger, Edmund C., *Desert Wildlife*. Stanford, Calif., Stanford University Press, 1962.

Kebbe, Chester E., "The Bounty System in Oregon." *Oregon State Game Commission Bulletin*, Vol. 13, No. 11 (November, 1958), pp. 3-4.

Lauckart, J. Burton, "Predator Management." Unpublished paper read before Conference of Western Association of State Game and Fish Commissioners, Santa Fe, N.M., June 13, 1961.

Leopold, A. Starker, *Wildlife of Mexico*. Berkeley, University of California Press, 1959.

Marston, M. A., "Winter Relations of Bobcats to White-tailed Deer in Maine." *Journal of Wildlife Management*, 6:328 (1942).

Matson, J. R., "(Bob) Cats Kill Deer." *Journal of Mammalogy*, 29:69 (1948).

Bibliography

Milne, L. J. and M. J., *The World of Night*. New York, Harper and Brothers, 1948.

Moore, Joseph C., "Mammals from Welaka, Florida." *Journal of Mammalogy,* 27:55 (1946).

Patterson, Robert L., *The Sage Grouse in Wyoming*. Denver, Sage Books, Inc., 1952.

Penner, Lawrence R., and Parke, Wesley N., "Notoedric Mange in the Bobcat." *Journal of Mammalogy,* 35:459 (1954).

Pollack, E. Michael, "Breeding Habits of Bobcat in Northeastern United States." *Journal of Mammalogy,* 31:329 (1950).

Pollack, E. M., and Sheldon, W. G., *The Bobcat in Massachusetts.* Massachusetts Division of Fisheries and Game, 1951.

Robinson, Weldon B., and Grand, Eugene F., "Comparative Movements of Bobcats and Coyotes." *Journal of Wildlife Management,* 22:117 (1958).

Rollings, Clair T., "Habits, Foods, and Parasites of the Bobcat in Minnesota." *Journal of Wildlife Management,* 9:131 (1945)

Seton, Ernest Thompson, *Lives of Game Animals*. Boston, Charles T. Branford Company, 1909.

————, "Bobcats and Wild Turkeys." *Journal of Mammalogy,* 1:140 (1920).

Silver, Helenette, *A History of New Hampshire Game and Furbearers*. New Hampshire Fish and Game Department, 1957.

Tische, Jim, "Trail of the Big Cat." *Outdoor Nebraska,* Vol. 37, No. 3 (March, 1959).

Trippensee, R. E., *Wildlife Management*. New York, McGraw-Hill Book Company, Inc., 1953.

Bibliography

Ulmer, Fred A., Jr., "Melanism in the Felidae." *Journal of Mammalogy,* 22:285 (1941).

Weaver, Richard Lee, "Attacks on Porcupine by Gray Fox and Wildcats." *Journal of Mammalogy,* 20:379 (1939).

Young, Stanley P., *The Bobcat of North America.* The Stackpole Company, Harrisburg, Pa., and The Wildlife Management Institute, Washington, D. C., 1958.

2450